FRESH
MEAT

VIKING
*an imprint of*
PENGUIN BOOKS

VIKING

Published by the Penguin Group
Penguin Books Ltd, 80 Strand, London WC2R 0RL, England
Penguin Group (USA) Inc., 375 Hudson Street, New York, New York 10014, USA
Penguin Group (Canada), 90 Eglinton Avenue East, Suite 700, Toronto, Ontario, Canada M4P 2Y3
(a division of Pearson Penguin Canada Inc.)
Penguin Ireland, 25 St Stephen's Green, Dublin 2, Ireland (a division of Penguin Books Ltd)
Penguin Group (Australia) 707 Collins Street, Melbourne, Victoria 3008, Australia
(a division of Pearson Australia Group Pty Ltd)
Penguin Books India Pvt Ltd, 11 Community Centre,
Panchsheel Park, New Delhi – 110 017, India
Penguin Group (NZ), 67 Apollo Drive, Rosedale, Auckland 0632, New Zealand
(a division of Pearson New Zealand Ltd)
Penguin Books (South Africa) (Pty) Ltd, Block D, Rosebank Office Park,
181 Jan Smuts Avenue, Parktown North, Gauteng 2193, South Africa

Penguin Books Ltd, Registered Offices: 80 Strand, London WC2R 0RL, England

www.penguin.com

First published 2012
001

Copyright © Objective Productions, 2012

The moral right of the author has been asserted

Set in Beton
Typeset by Estuary English
Printed in Spain by Industria Gráfica Cayfosa, SA
Colour reproduction by Altaimage

A CIP catalogue record for this book is available from the British Library

ISBN: 978–0–670–92214–7

# FRESH MEAT

The Essential Guide
for ~~New Undergraduates~~
THE FUTURE UNEMPLOYED

Jesse Armstrong, Sam Bain, Keith Akushie,
Jon Brown, Rose Heiney and Penny Skinner

VIKING
*an imprint of*
PENGUIN BOOKS

Faber and Faber
Bloomsbury House
74–77 Great Russell Street
London WC1B 3DA

Oregon M. Shawcross
28 Hartnell Road, Manchester

5 January 2012

Dear Editor-in-Chief

RE: **Fresh Meat**

Further to a telephone conversation with one of your colleagues in the reception department, I am writing to submit:

1. A covering letter introducing myself and my book (i.e. this thing you are reading)
2. My complete proposal for aforementioned book, as titled below:

### FRESH MEAT: The Essential Guide for New Undergraduates

I – Oregon M. Shawcross – am a revolutionary, in the truest sense of the word. And my intention is that this book should revolutionize not only the way students live their lives today, but also the way that we in this country publish books.

Gone are the stilted 'how to' guides of our predecessors. We, the internet generation, need a fast-paced, many-textured, multi-authored approach to reading. We want to feel we are not so much flicking, as clicking through the pages.

An extensive search of your website has revealed to me that while Faber and Faber currently publishes handbooks on (among others) Handel, Wagner, Shakespeare, ballet and the selected poems of T. S. Eliot, Faber does not represent an actual student guidebook. And take it from me, you – and your readers – are missing out!

And having spoken to my friends and peers, we agree that the existing books on the market are 'totes inadequate' (as we might say). My housemate Josie's mother bought her a book in her first term which called itself a 'Survival Guide' and – let me tell you – she fucked* up more than anyone! Was there a chapter on 'How to Identify a Love Rat Masquerading as a Virgin Masquerading as a Love Rat?' No! In other words, clearly that book is out of fucking* date.

It's spunky, it's funky, it's young and, most of all, it's fresh!

I believe this is exactly the sort of book that could bring Faber and Faber into the twenty-first century. You might even need me more than I need you (I have also sent this proposal to Bloomsbury and Penguin, but as the original publishers of *The Bell Jar*, you are my first choice).

Yours sincerely

*Oregon* x

Oregon M. Shawcross
Student and Poet

*Excuse my fucking language, but you know what, Faber and Faber? GET USED TO IT. *Fresh Meat* is a no-holds-barred, genital-warts-and-all exposé of the reality of modern student life. And yeah, there's gonna be some bad language . . .

# FRESH MEAT

By Oregon M. Shawcross

With contributions from:

Jonathan 'JP' Pembersley
Josie Jones
Howard MacCallum
Violet 'Vod' Nordstrom
Kingsley Owen

1. Introduction – Oregon M. Shawcross humorously discusses the various different types of student, from naive school leavers, to mature students, to the more sophisticated 'gap-year gang'. She advises you on who to make friends with, and who to avoid at all costs.

2. Oregon M. Shawcross has collected a series of writings and musings from her peers and will present these as a carefully orchestrated montage, designed to create a complete vision of the reality of student life today. Is it a guide? Is it an explosion of artistic expression from the cream of the crop of today's young thinkers?* Yes. It is both! Material includes: recipes, real-life correspondence, fiction, poetry, as well as the how-tos from real-life students who – let's face it – are better placed than anyone else to offer our readers advice.

3. Oregon M. Shawcross amusingly concludes the melange with a brief concluding chapter, discussing what we have learned from the *Fresh Meat* guide, and how we might take those lessons forward into our everyday lives . . . just kidding. That's what you would expect, right? This book will intentionally NOT have a conclusion because the university experience, as with life, is far too fluid and complicated to be summed up or to have a neat ending.

* Regrettably, now roughly 40% of youth are 'getting into uni', but the students here at Manchester are in the top per cent of that 40%, and it's not true that lots of us applied to Oxbridge and didn't get in. If you must know? Yes, I did apply to Cambridge. But I rejected THEM. As soon as I'd had my interview. So there!

# THANKS FOR READING!

# Contents

Part One    Survival Guide    9

Part Two    Out of the Lecture Hall    81

Part Three    Food & Drink    153

Part Four    Making Your Money Last    175

# Part One

# Survival Guide

# Introduction

**By Oregon M. Shawcross**

OK, guys, listen up...

Believe me, 'judgemental' is the LAST thing I am, but sometimes in life it's necessary to make quick decisions. And the first day of uni is that time. Friendships in this context happen fast, and you don't want to end up stuck with a load of bad 'uns from day one, week one.

So here's my quick and easy guide to identifying what I am humorously calling 'The Different Species of Student Animals' – with illustrations by Violet Nordstrom. (Memo: get Vod to finish fucking pictures!)

## The home-leaver animal

These students are usually aged 18 and have never lived away from home before. Bless them. They will have no clue how to boil a kettle or use a washing machine, and have probably only been abroad on a school trip.

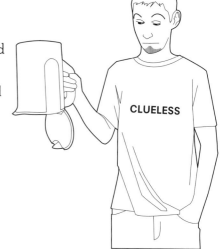

Make friends if the home leaver seems on your wavelength, but be prepared to share your wisdom and experience – as well as show them how to use the grill!

**Befriendability:** ★★★☆☆ Could become real friends

## The academic creature

These students have come here to work. Yawn. Most likely they will spend their whole time locked in their rooms with all the best library books, having failed to realize that term three of year three is the time to knuckle down, and any serious studying done before that is a shameful waste of 'the best years of your life'. Avoid.

**Befriendability:** ★☆☆☆☆ Useful during exam time

## The mature beast

This beast is unlikely to be found in student accommodation or in the pub after lectures. However, it is worth noting that if you do encounter a mature student in the pub then they are likely to be flush with cash and eager to get a round in. Possibly more true of the male of the species, who may be experiencing a life crisis and be keen to befriend young, hot, sexy students who make him look hip and cool.

**Befriendability:** ★★☆☆☆
Great for getting a round in

## The gap-year gang

Hurray, some like-minded individuals! With fascinating stories, too. If you see a white man with dreadlocks or a girl wearing rainbow trousers, then run to them and insist on introducing yourself – these could be your true friends for life.

Sadly, I haven't managed to meet nearly enough of these, as I narrowly missed getting my place in halls, and subsequent attempts to join the gap-year gang haven't quite worked out. Ultimately, they are way cool and perfectly reasonably have a tight-knit friendship core and can't just admit anyone to this inner circle.

But I do see them around campus, on their amazing unicycles, doing their FAB juggling, and constantly wish I had managed to make friends with them in the beginning. Next year I'm learning to fire-twirl. I think that will clinch it.

**Befriendability:** ★★★★★ Get in there quick!

Prof. J. M. Barnard
Admissions department
Gonville and Caius College
University of Cambridge
Cambridge
Cambridgeshire

Oregon M. Shawcross

A different, probably better university

Somewhere else

3 March 2012

Dear Professor Barnard,

Thank you for your letter dated 3 January 2011, and apologies for the delay in replying. The reason for my slowness is that I forgot I'd ever received it – that's how little thought I've given the matter. It barely registered. Anyway, in the interests of refreshing both our memories, the gist of the letter was this: you deeply regretted that you were unable to offer me a place to read English Language and Literature at your college; competition had been intense and places were limited, and you wished me all the best for the future, etc.

I deeply regret to inform you that I am unable to accept your letter of rejection. You see, I cared so little for your establishment that after my interview I immediately decided to reject you (I simply forgot to post the letter). Anyway, basically, your rejection of me is invalid because I'd already rejected you in my mind, even if I hadn't yet found the time to contact you to say as much.

I thought it would be kind of me to write and let you know exactly why you and your establishment mildly disgust me. It may prove helpful, in case you want to improve your service in the future. Here are my reasons. First: age. Your college, in case you hadn't noticed, is very, very old, to the point that many of your buildings are, quite frankly, dangerous. The staircase leading to your office (where we met) was a death trap. Yes, the dark wood panels were attractive, but the 'medieval' stairs were so uneven we ought to have been given helmets before ascending. Perhaps this is deliberate, and the stairs present some sort of 'intellectual' puzzle for your Maths and Philosophy students. Well, good luck to them, but I nearly ended up with a broken nose. Which, incidentally, was the reason for my tears in the first interview – I wasn't upset by your questions, I was in actual physical pain because of the hazards of your so-called 'beautiful' buildings.

Secondly, snobbery. When it comes to literature you, my friend, are nothing more than a little Lord Snooty. Terrified of appearing thick, you seek out opportunities to belittle others. Why else would you have responded as you did when I expressed admiration for my favourite book, *The Horse Whisperer* by Nicholas Evans? If I remember rightly, and I may not (if you recall I couldn't give a monkeys one way or the other about any of this) you said that this work was 'not exactly canonical'. Whilst saying this, you clearly suppressed a sneer. Well, riddle me this. If *The Horse Whisperer* is, as you suggested, not as good as *Ulysses*, then why didn't the film of *Ulysses* gross $187 million worldwide, and star Robert Redford and a young Scarlett Johansson? Oh, yeah, that's right, they didn't make a film of *Ulysses*. BECAUSE IT WOULD HAVE BEEN RUBBISH.

Oh dear, oh dear. This really isn't looking good for you, is it? Well, you know what else isn't looking good? Cambridge. It's quite a third-rate town if we're honest. There's a sub-par Superdrug (even Luton's is bigger); a quite messy Next and a big queue at McDonalds (unfathomable, given that they don't even stock the limited edition Rolo McFlurries). I know that none of this is strictly your fault, but you should still know, so you can stop bragging about what a 'gem' of a city your college is in. It really is just a couple of churches Hitler would've liked, a not-very-big river and a lot of cobblestones (which you can just as easily find in Durham, St Andrews and, quite frankly, Aberystwyth).

Anyway, that's it, I think. I suppose all that remains for me to say is that I actually applied to your college as a joke. I was off my nut on absinthe and thought, Gonville and Caius, they sound like Muppet names. Ha ha ha. And woke up the next morning to find out I'd applied. Hilarious. I suppose that's just the final 'twist in the tale'. And to think you said I 'didn't understand narrative'.

Please don't be disheartened by this rejection. I really do wish you all the best for the future.

Yours sincerely,

*Oregon*

Oregon M. Shawcross

# Top Ten Tips for Having a Top Time at Uni!

**By Josie Jones**

My great friend Oregon has asked me to write something on the subject of how to settle in at uni, which I am more than happy to do!

I'm only recently a fresher myself, and have thoroughly enjoyed the act of joining university and entering studentsville, as we students call it! Here are my top tips for how to make the most of your time as a fresher:

1.  Arrive early – your uni friends (and therefore the friends you will have for the rest of your life) will be the first people you bump into when you arrive, so it's important to be there in plenty of time.

2.  To help you 'bump into people' and make friends, open the door to your bedroom and put your stereo on nice and loud! This encourages people to see you as a friendly and lively presence – someone who is more than happy to party. Not being happy to party can lead to you being labelled a loser and becoming a social leper.

3.  Along the same lines, it is important to drink as much as possible in your first few weeks/months of uni. You must demonstrate that you are 'up for it' and not a saddo who is going to concentrate too much on studying. Studying is for later. Remember: you've got three years for all that. In these early days your social life is the focus, and rightly so.

4.  Try not to worry if you feel lonely, homesick, suicidal, or as though you have made the worst mistake of your whole life by

Be careful about choosing your friends, or you might end up with a bunch of tools like these for three years.

Or worse, like these.

coming to uni. You might well have made a mistake – after all, many graduates won't get a good job and will end up in loads of debt – but the feeling that you've made a terrible mistake will start to fade once you get into the cycle of too much drinking/recovering from too much drinking/starting to drink too much again. So don't worry.

5.  The Freshers' fair is a great place to join societies and is good for meeting people when your new best friends (the people you first bumped into) start to piss you off.

6.  Somewhere on campus will be a doctor specially designated to look after students. They will be one of the meanest people you have ever met, and even if you are seriously ill, they will send you away with no medicine. So when you are dying of meningitis, or pregnant, or becoming schizophrenic, it is best to seek the help of a different GP, as the campus GP will most likely leave you to die.

7.  Go and explore the local area. Many students will warn you against this one, as they are paranoid about people from the nearest town who are 'not students' – names for these people include 'townies' and 'locals'. Some students are very

frightened of the locals, but try not to worry. They are in fact just normal people – like you were before you became a student – and will not necessarily kick you to death just for carrying an NUS card! I think getting to know the place you have moved to is a healthy way to feel more at home there.

Booze: that's the ticket.

8. Try not to have sex with people who live in the same halls/house as you. Uni is definitely a time for experimentation, but there's a time and a place for it – and in this instance, the old saying 'don't shit where you eat' is very relevant. Trust me on this.

9. Don't worry if the tutors appear not to give a shit about you, or know who you are, or anything about you. You are not alone. To clarify: you are not the only one they don't care about. You are, in fact, as far as the tutors are concerned, completely alone. But the feeling of abandonment does get easier as time passes (see Tip 4).

10. Finally, try not to worry too much about the fact that these are the best years of your life. I mean, I do worry about this quite a lot, because the idea that things get worse than this is a very depressing thought. But I think if you just forge ahead as though everything will work out fine in the end, then, you know, that can be as good an approach as any.

I hope that was useful. Like I say, I'm only new to this myself, so we can all learn together. Which is, after all, the idea of being . . . a student. Yay!

# Brian and Howard:
## A Friendship in Three Acts

The university social scene is a pressure cooker environment. Under these intense conditions, friendships can blossom out of nowhere, before contracting and exploding like white dwarves (the stars, not the people). In an extract from what would later constitute his full report to the Manchester Constabulary, Howard MacCallum recounts the harrowing details of the friendship that would come to define his first year at university . . .

## Term one: Genesis

**15 October**    Quantitative and Earth Materials seminar. A flame-haired young buck, full of vim and vigour, drops a geological zinger re: rates of sedimentation in the Arctic Ocean that leaves me quite literally choking on my Ginster's Buffet Bar.

**22 October**    More pin-sharp geological yucks; more semi-ingested meat-based foodstuffs. Then comes the bombshell: 'I'm Brian, would you like to know my gamer tag . . . ?'

**24 October**    The germ of our friendship multiplies like H1N1 in an Indonesian pigpen. Gamer tags, Facebook accounts, Twitter handles, mobile numbers. My diary entry reads: 'It's a whirlwind of Earth Science banter, and I'm utterly powerless to resist . . .'

**10 November**  Foam Party at the Union. The evening is spent savagely (but inaudibly) mocking our peers. Brian starts riffing on how he fantasizes about 'throwing a hand grenade' into the halls of residence. Drenched in sarcasm, he adds, 'I know where we can get one from. All we need is £300 and a secure postal address.' I laugh and laugh and laugh.

**11 December**   Diary entry reads: 'Pub warfare . . .' Josie's excellent ex-boyfriend Dave takes exception to Brian and grabs him harshly by the scrotie before head-butting him to the ground. Brian to me: 'Howard, do you have my back?' Me to Brian: 'No, Brian, I do not have your back . . .'

**12 December**   Brian sabotages my Tectonics exam by faking a letter informing me that my mother has been arrested on suspicion of murder in the first degree. Later, as I try to console my weeping mother, who's confused by the sudden offers of bail contributions from the wider MacCallum family, I come to the conclusion that my friendship with Brian is unhelpful for my delicate internal equilibrium.

**13 December**   I send an anonymous email to the accommodation officer: 'I have reason to suspect an imminent hand-grenade attack on the halls of residence. Suggest immediate ban on leaving all windows open and unattended.'

## Term two: Blacksliding

**15 January**   A chance encounter with Brian in the canteen. He delivers a pitch-perfect satirical takedown of the university's ultra-conservative fell-walking society that has me helpless with laughter. In spite of myself, I agree to a burger at the Canadian Charcoal Pit. My diary entry reads simply: 'Brian and I are back on terms . . . What have I done . . . ?'

**1 February**   I ignore a call from Brian. Later, during a game of *Call of Duty: Black Ops*, he blasts me in the face with a shotgun and dances on my corpse for an unnecessarily prolonged period. I find it oddly chilling.

**24 February**   Brian invites me to the cinema to see an advance screening of *Wrath of the Titans*. I politely decline. He explodes in a furious rage, during which he describes me as a 'traitorous cum-bucket' and a 'baby born of Satan's anus'. I end up going with him. It's OK, but the 3D is disappointing.

| | |
|---|---|
| **12 March** | Brian turns up drunk at the house at 3.23 a.m. demanding a game of Risk. I adopt the trusted 'Let the Wookie Win' strategy, and quickly concede Brazil and Greenland. My meekness only serves to infuriate him. He becomes physical. I inform Brian I am terminating our friendship with immediate effect. |
| **13 March** | As per Brian's request, I put into writing my desire to terminate our friendship with immediate effect. All ongoing projects – including blueprints for an underwater battle-tank and an iPhone app that tells you the distance to the nearest available go-karting facility – are put on ice. |

## Term three: Mind Games

| | |
|---|---|
| **17 April** | Oregon takes delivery of a takeaway pizza from a 'squat, small-eyed man-boy with terrible hair'. When I open the box I discover a Pepperoni Passion but with a difference . . . the tiny circles of cured sausage have been reconfigured to make what can only be described as a 'Meat Swastika'. I photograph it extensively (see exhibit A), then consume it. Afterwards I realize I had the camera set to video mode. I take low-resolution stills from the video footage, but it's not ideal. |

**EXHIBIT A**

The 'Meat Swastika' pizza.

**29 April**  Brian starts to bombard my inbox with Photoshopped images in which I appear to be having a three-way sex-transaction with two versions of myself (see exhibit B).

**30 April**  More Howard-on-Howard pornography.

**1 May**  Yet more Howard-on-Howard pornography. My diary entry reads: 'The level of detailing on one image in particular is so striking I find myself in despair – what a waste of a fine graphic designer!'

**3 May**  I open my monthly Orange phone bill to discover that I've been changed from the highly economical Dolphin call plan to the slightly less economical Panther call plan. Though an internal investigation proves fruitless, I nonetheless suspect the shadowy claw of Brian at play.

**28 May**  Brian is sighted crouching in the rear garden dressed entirely in black and carrying a large wooden mallet, the kind you might use to erect a circus tent. I explode into a fury, grab my nunchucks and head out. The following exchange takes place in the driving rain, with both of us shouting (in CAPS) . . .

**Me:**  BRIAN . . . THIS ENDS TONIGHT!
(I swing my nunchucks menacingly.)

**Brian:**  YOU BETRAYED ME!

**Me:** JUST LEAVE ME ALONE OR YOU'LL GET A TASTE OF THESE . . .
(I swing my nunchucks again.)

**Brian:** . . . ARE YOU OK? YOUR LIP IS BLEEDING.
(I had hit myself in the face with my nunchucks.)

**Brian:** LET ME GET YOU A TOWEL.
As Brian tends to my split lip, he opens up and apologizes for his campaign of terror. In that moment, we come to realize that our friendship is a toxic, poisonous influence, and one that threatens to drag both of us down into the swirling purple-black ether of the abyss.

**Brian:** Goodbye, Howard.

**Me:** Goodbye, Brian. (We shake hands, and walk away.)
My diary entry simply reads: 'Free at last, free at last. Thank God almighty I am free at last . . .'

Post-script: We've subsequently put all this behind us and are currently working on a new game-show format entitled *Beat the Bully*, in which former schoolyard ruffians are forced to compete in a series of humiliating academia-based quizzes against their intellectually superior former victims.

Dear Katie,

I have decided to give my diary a name so it feels more like a friend when I write in it.

Sunday, 9 October

And so it is that I, Josephine Jane Jones, am to become Dear Diary. How are you?

Sunday, 9 October

This is my diary. I am writing it. I haven't written one before, but Mum says it will be good for me while I settle into my new life at university. Not that my mum is the reason I am writing this. I don't just do stuff my mum says. Obviously

Sunday, 9 October
Dear Diary,

Tomorrow, I leave for Manchester, where I will be studying to become a real-life dentist! I can't wait. Dave is coming over in a bit to have our 'last night together'. I am going to miss him so much, it's going to be so weird without him. He is the love of my life.

Bit bored of writing now so will go and eat some cheese. Will write more tomorrow from...
MY NEW HOUSE: 28 Hartnell Road, Manchester
M— (will fill in post code when know it).

Monday, 10 October

Dear Diary,

It is really ~~weird here~~. I ~~don't know if I like anyone. The house smells~~ funny. The house is really cool and I am settling in well. There are two girls, Vod and Oregon. So far they are nice and friendly. The one called Vod is definitely a lesbian. ~~So exciting! Goodbye valleys, hello cosmopolitan life!~~ I am cool with this, though might not tell Dave in case he gets jealous/possessive. Pretty sure we will soon be best of friends, friends for life, and one day we will sit and read this diary together and laugh about it. Can't wait.

The blokes are OK so far — Kingsley, who seems nice, ~~quite good looking~~, and Howard, who came with the house. I think he's some kind of post-grad or mature student or something. Either way, he's got a beard. And he is ~~quite weird~~ a cool guy.

Spent most of the afternoon on the phone to Dave. I miss him so much. Don't know how I will get through the next three years without him. We have made each other a promise of complete faithfulness. He's really worried about me being away etc., but I know for a fact that Dave is the One. I will have no ~~trouble~~ trouble whatsoever being faithful to him.

Tuesday, 11 October

Oops. Accidentally shagged fellow housemate. ARGH! To be fair to self, didn't realize was housemate until after regrettable sex had occurred. Then, next morning, realized. Too late!

JP is from Devon and he went to boarding school. My dad would be so disappointed in me. To be fair, I was even more twatted than when I ♥Dave♥ shagged Neil Jones in Year II at Laura Froggett's Wild West BBQ. Although at least this time I wasn't dressed as half a buffalo.[1]

As a side note, didn't know willies could be so long and thin! JP's was much longer and thinner than Dave's — which in comparison is quite short and stocky. Interestingly, this reflects their actual appearance as JP is much taller and thinner than Dave.

So far am not doing well with promise to be faithful to Dave. Out of one night away from him, I have been unfaithful one time. That's a 100% betrayal statistic. Must try harder.

NB. In the event that me and Dave end up married, entry above must not be included if/when this diary is published as part of my Famous Dentist Memoirs (title TBC)

Hope me and Dave end up married. I love him so much, with all my heart.

Think I am in love with Kingsley, the other boy from the house. He is so sensitive and listens really well, not like Dave, who always interrupts me before I finish my sentence.

Kingsley is also quite good looking, although hairless. Do I fancy a hairless chest? I think I do. Perhaps love conquers all.

[1] Front half

Thursday, 13 October
Freshers' Fair!
Have signed up for the following societies: Aid and Save
Animal Planet, Amateur Boxing Club, Amateur Dramatic
Club, American Football Club, Americas Archaeology
Group (formerly Andean Archaeology Group), Amnesty
International, Anglo-Saxon Norse and Celtic Society,
Anime and Manga Society, Arabic Society, Archaeological
Field Club, Architecture Sans Frontières.

Was still working my way round the 'A' section
when the fair closed, so haven't yet signed up for
Nightline or the student newspaper. But will go back
next time and do that!


Sunday, 16 October
Spoke to Dave on phone just now. Interruptions before
end of my sentence: 10! So annoying. Can't believe
didn't annoy me more before. Has always been bit
annoying, but previously felt it was spontaneous, exciting
Dave. Now realize it's just ADHD Dave.

Me and K have been chatting through the glory
hole. He is so funny. He spent ages caring for his mum.
It's such an amazing quality in a bloke: caring.
Wonder what his willy is like?

**Friday**, 21 October

Sorry haven't written for a while, went home to visit. Was nice to eat some vegetables, though Dave was really crowding me.

Have either gone off sex or gone off Dave. Think the latter, as can't stop thinking about sex with Kingsley.

Bet he's really good in bed. Bet he is v good at down below. Not like Dave, who eats pussy like he eats everything else — loud and speedy.

Kingsley is a VIRGIN! Can't believe didn't know this. At school we could always tell the boys who were virgins because they had smaller muscles and paler skin. Actually — Kingsley is quite pale and not that muscly — but this is also true of JP, who is definitely NOT a virgin (oops) — all of which leads me to suspect that my methods of virgin detection are unreliable.

Can't decide if K being a virgin makes me fancy him more or less.

I think, weirdly, more. Sign I am definitely in love with him, as mere physical infatuation would probably be extinguished by the realization of his sexual incompetence.

Instead am preoccupied by imaginings of breaking his virginity.

Gotta go. Promised Dave would call him by nine.

**Tuesday**, 1 November

Am thinking of breaking up with Dave. (Please delete this entry for memoirs if me and Dave are still together.)

Don't miss him at all, and speaking to him on the phone has become a chore. Everything he does or says annoys me.

Interruptions today: 13!!!

## 2 CONFIDENTIAL Student sexual health questionnaire

**Name:** (you do not have to complete this)

Josie

**Indicate your gender:**

Female

**Indicate your age:**

20

**Are you sexually active?**

Yes

**Do you use contraception every time you have sex?**

Absolutely

**Indicate which form of contraception you use?** I'm on the pill, but before that we used condoms. Which was always fine, apart from one time when the condom broke and I was so scared I was pregnant that I tried to give myself a DIY abortion with parsley. I've never told anyone that before. Please don't tell anyone that.

**Where do you purchase your contraception** Any one of the major chemists, apart from once when Dave and I were drunk and got some condoms from the corner shop. But they were a weird brand and the box was dusty and I got so freaked out that I couldn't have sex at all that night.

*Is it the same thing? That's always confused me.

## 3

** (Though sometimes at night I do think I can still feel or hear them).

**Have you recently suffered from any of the following sexually transmitted diseases that you are aware of?**

| HIV / AIDS | Syphillis | Gonorrhea | Herpes |
|---|---|---|---|
| Oh my God, No. | NO | NO | No, but I had a cold sore last month. That's herpes, isn't it? But it was on my face. * |

| Chlamydia | Hepatitis B or C | Other (please specify) |
|---|---|---|
| NO | NO | I broke up with my first boyfriend after he gave me crabs, but that was four years ago so they're definitely all gone now* * |

**Have you recently had unprotected oral or anal sex?** Yes. I have received oral sex, but it was so unpleasurable I doubt it even counts as sex. Also, how could you 'protect' that? Would it be one of those dental dam things? Because I've never understood how those work. I am quite curious, though, as I'm a dental student and it seems relevant. I wouldn't mind a chat about this with you at some point, if it were convenient.

**Where do you get most of your information on sexual health?**

Reputable sexual health websites and women's magazines.

**Would you say you are well informed about your sexual health?** Absolutely. Apart from the dental dam thing, but no one really understands that, do they? I mean, why is it called a dam? A dam implies, like, flood water. Eww. Gross.

**Do you have any other comments?**

I found this questionnaire informative and entertaining to complete.

## 2 CONFIDENTIAL Student sexual health questionnaire

**Name:** (you do not have to complete this)

Kingsley

**Indicate your gender:**

Male

**Indicate your age:**

19

**Are you sexually active?**

Yes

**Do you use contraception every time you have sex?**

Yes. Absolutely.
It's a very important part of being a responsible sexual man, I think.

**Indicate which form of contraception you use?**

Condoms.
I like to take responsibility, as a man, for the contraceptive arrangements.

**Where do you purchase your contraception**

I suppose from the nearest chemist to wherever I'm about to have sex. So, a variety of different chemists all over the country!

**3**

**Have you recently suffered from any of the following sexually transmitted diseases that you are aware of?**

| HIV / AIDS | Syphilis | Gonorrhea | Herpes |
|---|---|---|---|
| No | No | No | No |

| Chlamydia | Hepatitis B or C | Other (please specify) No | |
|---|---|---|---|
| No | No | Phew – It seems I've had a long series of lucky sexual escapes (not necessarily lucky, actually, given how responsible and mature I am about my sexual health) | |

**Have you recently had unprotected oral or anal sex?**

Yes, absolutely. But I made sure that she and I had the 'big sexual health chat' before the fun kicked off (as is usual, I believe).

**Where do you get most of your information on sexual health?**

I generally discuss the issue with one of my many sexual partners.

**Would you say you are well informed about your sexual health?**

Hugely so.
I run a very tight ship, sexual health-wise.

**Do you have any other comments?**

When I said I'd recently had anal sex, obviously I meant giving it rather than receiving! I mean, everybody's free to do what they want with their own body, but I wouldn't want you getting the wrong impression. Thanks.

## 2 CONFIDENTIAL Student sexual health questionnaire

**Name:** (you do not have to complete this)

JP

**Indicate your gender:**

100% male.

**Indicate your age:** 19, aka my sexual. prime.

**Are you sexually active?** Hell, yeah. Like a motherfucking rap star.

**Do you use contraception every time you have sex?**

sire a brood it will be Deffo. When I with a very select mare. I've got family money to consider. Capiche?

**Indicate which form of contraception you use?**

Condoms (XXL size, preferably ribbed, never, ever flavoured).

**Where do you purchase your contraception** Boots. Or, sometimes, when I go to my Dad's barber for a shave in the hols, he gives me 'something for the weekend'. But they're totally the same brand as the ones in Boots, just in this little monogrammed wallet.

But my mate Jonty got it on his gap year and his balls swelled up to the size of fucking melons. It was hilarious.

**3**

**Have you recently suffered from any of the following sexually transmitted diseases that you are aware of?**

Hold on, you're not going to put the needle up my dick, are you? Please don't put the needle up my dick.

| HIV / AIDS | Syphilis | Gonorrhea | Herpes |
|---|---|---|---|
| No. | No. What am I, a medieval hooker? | Is that the clap? No. * | No. Please don't put the needle up my dick. |

| Chlamydia | Hepatitis B or C | Other (please specify) |
|---|---|---|
| No. | Isn't that a heroin-addict disease? No. | There is really absolutely no need to put the needle up my dick. |

**Have you recently had unprotected oral or anal sex?**

Whichever answer will mean that you don't put the needle up my dick.

**Where do you get most of your information on sexual health?**

Lorn. No, I'm kidding. My Mum? No, that's weird. I don't know. My school matron? Please don't put the needle up my dick.

**Would you say you are well informed about your sexual health?**

Well informed enough that you don't have to put the needle up my dick.

**Do you have any other comments?**

If you try to put the needle up my dick I will call the police. My uncle is a lawyer. Don't say I didn't warn you.

# Student Counselling
## Case-Study: Jonathan Pembersley

Far away from home, and placed under almost intolerable social, financial and academic pressure, it's no surprise that almost one third of students will seek the solace of the campus counsellors. As these notes from JP's case file show, there can be many reasons why one might take a seat on the therapist's couch.

Oregon

# University Counselling services
## Initial assessment

Forename: _I_

Surname: _P_

**Why do you feel you need therapy?**

I need counselling because I'm just bloody gutted about the death of my father. It's like I've lost my right arm (and I'm right-handed, so you can imagine how difficult that must be for me).

**Are you experiencing any of the following:**

• Sadness?

Erm, I'm a bloody orphan – what do you think?!

• Loss of pleasure?

Last night I was watching Mission Impossible: Ghost Protocol and I suddenly found myself blubbing like a little girl. All I could mutter to myself through the heavy bog of snot and tears was, 'Daddy liked watching films ...'

Form: UMC127A/Referral

Continued overleaf:

• Suicidal thoughts?

Right now I'm fantasizing about jamming
this Bic Biro into my jugular and spraying
the magnolia walls of your office with a
thick, clotty coating of type-O negative
before slumping dead onto this very form.
If that's suicidal, then yes.

• Punishment feelings?

During my darker moments (which are all
the time), I feel like maybe Jesus took
my dad from me as a punishment for the sins
and indiscretions of my youth. (I once shot
a man during a grouse hunt. He subsequently
died. However, despite two formal inquests, at the
time of writing there is _no_ concrete link
between my maiming and his eventual demise.)

## Initial assessment: continuation

• Self-dislike?

I, Jonathan Pembersley, am a worthless shit.
I'm a waste of time and space, like a dead fly
laying belly-up in an empty bottle of
Corona (death again. Why am I _so_ obsessed
with death?!). In fact, they should take
all of my functioning body parts and recycle
them to make a worthwhile human who has
something to contribute to society, other than
just sitting around in his Calvins playing
FIFA 12 while weeping uncontrollably about
Roger fucking Pembersley (RIP).

• Crying?

Do I cry? How about this...

... _actual_ tears. All I had to do was
think about the hole in my heart the
size of a shotgun blast now that I'm
completely and irrevocably fatherless.
See, another one!

• Irritability?

A list of people I've told to 'fuck off'
in the last 48 hours :
1. Kingsley 2. Oregon 3. Howard (x5)
4. Josie 5. Vod
6. Myself, in the mirror, repeatedly,
while shirtless.

I'm just so fucking DEPRESSED about
this whole situation. It's like it's
raining misery and I'm the only one
who's left the house without an umbrella
and I'm just getting soaked through to
the skin by these big fat wet globules
of liquid sadness. In conclusion, I feel
unable to partake in my forthcoming
Geology exam and hereby request that I
be excused on the grounds of my
chronic, debilitating grief.

Best JL

# University Counselling services
## Counseller's assessment

**Patient's name:** JONATHAN PEMBERSLEY

**Patient assessment:**

The patient presented himself as suffering from the extreme emotional fallout from the recent death of his father. It very quickly became apparent to me, however, that the patient was in fact using his grief as a pretext to avoid his forthcoming Geology exam. Post session, I liaised with his Geology professor to arrange a postponement of the exam. The patient subsequently turned up at my office in some form of genuine distress and confusion and apparently propositioned me, suggesting at one point that I was 'wet for him'. I declined his offer and made an appointment to see him the following week. The treatment is ongoing. Progress is slow and I am presently less than confident about making any significant headway.

**Counsellor's signature**

*Carol Smith*

Form: UMC 127B/Assessment

Howard MacCallum
28 Hartnell Road
Manchester

Dr G. Inishmore
Head of Department of Philosophy
Manchester Medlock University

13 July 2011

Dear Dr Inishmore,

On your departmental web page, the introduction to the undergraduate Philosophy course begins as follows: 'Have you ever wondered if there's a difference between knowing something and believing it? Are you concerned with how to tell right from wrong? Or have you perhaps reflected that right and wrong don't really exist?'

My response to all these questions is 'yes', which is why I immediately applied to study with you, so that I could, at last, find out the answers.

However, I have to tell you that after no less than three terms under your tutelage, and with a lecture attendance record of 96% (according to my personal stats) I remain none the wiser. In fact, I would go so far as to say that thus far my study of philosophy has done little except stir up more questions:

- Why are we here?
- More specifically: why are we here and not there?
- If I believe my own lie, does that make it true?
- What if it's all in my mind?
- If I decide it is all in my mind, will I be penalized for not handing in my essay on external reality?
- Which is better, Orange Cheddar or Yellow Cheddar?

I have become frustrated with the department's unwillingness to commit to definitive truths on all of the above, and to my final question, which I put to Dr Eccles in the car park after Thursday's lecture: Of all the known philosophies, which is the best?

Her response shocked me to the core. Not only did she appear reluctant to discuss this key issue, she began by asking me to 'define best'. Horrified, I referred her to the *Oxford English Dictionary* and walked away in disgust.

I therefore tender my resignation from the department. I am going to apply for Geology, which I hope will have a more solid foundation, as well as a teaching staff with a superior grasp of basic vocabulary.

Yours, with regret,

*Mac Callum*

Howard MacCallum

# So You've Chosen English Literature...
## An advisary guide

### By Violet Nordstrom

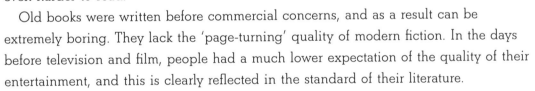

Well done. You've chosen a degree with a very small number of working hours per week. Many of the lectures are non-compulsory, and you will most likely be free to dedicate a massive amount of your time at university to partying.

The main problem with your degree[1] is the number of *books* you will be expected to read, some of which you will then need to write *essays* on.

Books tend to be long and contain many words. Reading them can be time-consuming, especially when dealing with old books, which are often poorly edited and have pages numbering in the high hundreds. The font can also be tiny, making them even harder to read.

Old books were written before commercial concerns, and as a result can be extremely boring. They lack the 'page-turning' quality of modern fiction. In the days before television and film, people had a much lower expectation of the quality of their entertainment, and this is clearly reflected in the standard of their literature.

Here are some things you might find helpful:

1. Whenever possible, choose to study books that have been adapted for TV/made into film. Watching them on telly is preferable to reading the book itself, and provides as good an understanding of what happens in the plot.

2. ALWAYS buy the book before going to a seminar, even if you do not intend to read

---

1. Aside from the fact that it will qualify you for nothing while costing a large amount of money.

it. Turning up without a copy of the book is an obvious giveaway that you haven't read it.

3. ALWAYS bend the book and highlight a few pages before the seminar. This gives the impression of careful and studious reading of the text.

If you are unable to watch a TV adaptation, then consider the following advice:

1. Before the seminar, consult a plot synopsis of the book on the internet. Use a reputable site such as Wikipedia, so you are familiar with the rough outline of what happens in the story. Google a few discussion points, so you will be aware of the kinds of subjects that might come up in class.

2. Read the opening chapter, the closing chapter and a few pages from the middle of the novel. Together with the plot synopsis, this is an adequate amount of study to survive in a seminar setting.

3. If you can be bothered, skim-read the sections in between, just in case something interesting stands out. Information gleaned through skim-reading should not be used for initiating conversation in seminars, but can be useful when joining an existing discussion. 'I remember that page!' you can say, and it will sound convincing.

4. When the seminar begins, immediately kick-start a conversation about the 'opening' of the novel. You can then remain quiet for the rest of the session, confident that you have established yourself as an intellectual presence.

5. Adopt an extreme stance in seminar discussions. Being someone with a strong opinion suggests a student who is passionate about their subject: e.g., '*Wuthering Heights* would have been better if Ralph Fiennes had done the voice-over.' Not necessarily something you believe about the book, but a valid viewpoint that will earn you respect.

6. Avoid modules with titles such as 'the Great European Novel'. This could not only involve long, old books, but is likely to include books translated from other languages. Definitely try to avoid Russian novels, as these are not only really long but contain very confusing character names, which are much harder to skim-read/ blag in essays/seminar setting.

7. Choose modules that include plays and/or poetry. This will involve far less reading, as these tend to be much shorter and contain fewer words.

# Vod's Guide to Literature

The first thing the prospective English Literature student should know is this: books are fucking long. The second thing they should know is this: some of them are fucking long and totally shit. So how do you know the good books that are worth reading from the shit books that aren't? Simple – you follow my handy guide to literature. I've read the books so you don't have to.*

* Not literally

| Title | Amount read | Synopsis | Verdict |
| --- | --- | --- | --- |
| *Hamlet* | 1½ of 5 acts. | Man-boy mopes about; sees ghost. | Like a really boring episode of *Midsomer Murders* set in Denmark. |
| *The Great Gatsby* | 17 pages, front cover, back cover, inside flap. | A man has some parties. | I saw this bloke reading it on the tram once and he had those long, pointy sideburns. Clearly a book for wankers. |
| *Midnight's Children* | 62 pages, three Amazon reviews. | A kid with a nose like a cucumber finds out he can read people's minds. Yes, really. | I'm sorry, no. I'm with the Muslims on this one. I want to fatwa his fat arse just for making me sit through this pile of festering horseshit. |

| Title | Amount read | Synopsis | Verdict |
|---|---|---|---|
| **A Christmas Carol** | I watched the film adaptation *Scrooged*, starring Bill Murray. | A TV executive gets visited by a ghost who's a taxi driver. In the end, Bill Murray has a change of heart and decides to give his brother a VCR instead of a set of crappy towels. | Hilarious. |
| **The Curious Incident of the Dog in the Night-time** | 33 pages, the Wikipedia entry. | A boy with mentalism issues finds a dead dog. | The Curious Incident of the Shit Book in the Night-time. |
| **A Heartbreaking Work of Staggering Genius** | 17 pages, a thing on a website. | Some fuckheads get cancer; they die. | A Heartbreaking Work of Staggering Bullshit. |
| **Oedipus Rex** | Oregon's essay. | Boy fucks mum. | Pretty good. |
| **Lolita** | 11 pages, overheard conversation in library. | Man fucks girl. | A bit like *When Harry Met Sally*, but for paedos. |

| Title | Amount read | Synopsis | Verdict |
|-------|-------------|----------|---------|
| *Lord of the Flies* | 36 pages of the York Notes. | A load of kids go mental on an island. It's the pre-teen *Inbetweeners* movie. | If I wanted to read about feral kids kicking down social taboos, I'd dig out my old diaries. |
| *Moby Dick* | Listened to about 20 minutes of the audiobook. | A bloke gets obsessed with a whale. | What kind of prick gets obsessed with a whale? |
| *Of Mice and Men* | I saw that bloke who used to present *Stars in Their Eyes* on *This Morning*, talking about being in the stage play. | The tragic, touching tale of a fuckwit who kills a girl then gets shot in the back of the head by his mate. | With respect to John Steinbeck, it sounded a bit shit. |
| *Fifty Shades of Grey* | The whole thing. | Grot. | Not grotty enough. |
| *Little Women* | 39 minutes of the TV adaptation. | A load of small girls buy a magical caravan that can reverse the flow of time. They go on adventures and solve historical crimes. | I'll be honest, I'd just taken some pretty heavy mushrooms and I hadn't slept in 72 hours, so it's all a bit hazy. I liked the bit with the Kraken. |

# Howard's Flowchart 1:
## Schematic when you like a girl

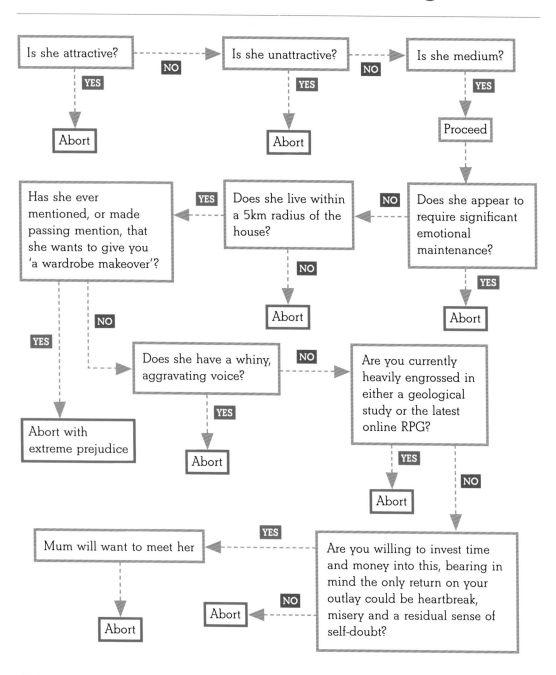

Is she attractive? --- NO ---> Is she unattractive? --- NO ---> Is she medium?

Is she attractive? YES ---> Abort

Is she unattractive? YES ---> Abort

Is she medium? YES ---> Proceed

Proceed ---> Does she appear to require significant emotional maintenance?

Does she appear to require significant emotional maintenance? NO ---> Does she live within a 5km radius of the house?

Does she appear to require significant emotional maintenance? YES ---> Abort

Does she live within a 5km radius of the house? YES ---> Has she ever mentioned, or made passing mention, that she wants to give you 'a wardrobe makeover'?

Does she live within a 5km radius of the house? NO ---> Abort

Has she ever mentioned, or made passing mention, that she wants to give you 'a wardrobe makeover'? YES ---> Abort with extreme prejudice

Has she ever mentioned, or made passing mention, that she wants to give you 'a wardrobe makeover'? NO ---> Does she have a whiny, aggravating voice?

Does she have a whiny, aggravating voice? YES ---> Abort

Does she have a whiny, aggravating voice? NO ---> Are you currently heavily engrossed in either a geological study or the latest online RPG?

Are you currently heavily engrossed in either a geological study or the latest online RPG? YES ---> Abort

Are you currently heavily engrossed in either a geological study or the latest online RPG? NO ---> Are you willing to invest time and money into this, bearing in mind the only return on your outlay could be heartbreak, misery and a residual sense of self-doubt?

Are you willing to invest time and money into this, bearing in mind the only return on your outlay could be heartbreak, misery and a residual sense of self-doubt? NO ---> Abort

Are you willing to invest time and money into this, bearing in mind the only return on your outlay could be heartbreak, misery and a residual sense of self-doubt? YES ---> Mum will want to meet her

Mum will want to meet her ---> Abort

# Kingsley's guide to drama for the non-exhibitionist

By Kingsley Owen

At some point in your university life you'll more than likely find yourself changing courses mid-term just to impress a girl or to prove something indefinable to a housemate. If you end up taking drama and, like me, you happen to be well adjusted and not an attention-craving approval-whore, your daily student life will be transformed into an obstacle course of a thousand miniature humiliations. Here are my top five tips for the non-exhibitionist drama student.

1. **Avoid the 'clowning' module:** there's an ancient tradition in clowning called the 'Circle of Fire'. Scared yet? You should be. Here's what happens. You stand all alone, pale and shaking, in the middle of a circle of 12 of your peers, including some incredibly attractive girls and some boys who hate you for unspecified reasons (probably because they're already receding and you aren't), and guess what? You're not allowed to exit the circle until you've made every person laugh. Each and every last prematurely balding one of them. I, Kingsley, currently hold the record for the longest period of time ever spent inside a Circle of Fire. Five hours, 32 minutes and 15 seconds. A whole five and a half hours of larking, joking, dancing, begging, pleading, shouting, swearing, introspecting and sobbing, interspersed with prolonged bouts of pacing. Technically, I was never released from the Circle of Fire. The Circle instead was mercifully dissolved when a Pilates class turned up to use the hall.

   In my darkest, most strangulating dreams, I'm back inside the Circle and I'm on my stomach, mugging and flapping, doing an impression of a cockney dolphin, hot tears of frustration and anger and hate streaming on to my T-shirt and making my collar damp, straining my every sinew to get a fucking laugh out of David fucking South. I wake up before he even cracks a smile.

2. **Wear a vest:** you never know when you and your classmates will be required to get undressed. This is both the blessing and the curse of the male drama student. Make sure your undergarments are clean and in full working order, and that your socks are free from Simpsons characters or funny slogans about how much you like to party.

3. **Take the 'noun' roles:** the best dramatic roles for the non-exhibitionist tend to be those listed in the character breakdown simply as a noun. 'Policeman' is a good part. 'Doctor' is fine. 'Inspector' is usually pretty safe, so long as you're not inspecting anything integral to the plot. (I once made the mistake of putting myself forward for the part of inspector in the play *The Inspector Calls*, only to find I had SHIT-LOADS OF LINES.) Of all the noun roles, the high watermark is 'passer-by'. You enter, you say your line, you pass by. That's it. You've done your bit. You've passed by. Take a bow.

   One note of caution: be wary of any role listed as an adjective and a noun. 'angry man', for instance, might only have three lines, but they will each require you to convey a specific emotion (in this case anger) and as such should be avoided at all costs.

4. **Cultivate a 'delicate sensibility'**: if you research the material you're being asked to perform ahead of time, and you're prepared ruthlessly to exploit the good nature of your fellow man by artfully weaving a series of elaborate and often heartbreaking lies, you can talk your way out of pretty much any dramatic production you care to mention. Here's how I might get out of a role in Arthur Miller's *The Death of a Salesman*: 'My dad was a salesman and he committed suicide in my back garden. It's still very raw'; Romeo and Juliet: 'My best friend at school was in a gang and he killed himself and then killed his girlfriend. It's still very raw'; *Waiting for Godot*: 'When I was three my granddad took me to the zoo. He went off to use the toilet. I sat and waited by the penguins for him to come back. I waited and waited. I was waiting there until closing time. They eventually found him keeled over in the toilet cubicle. Ever since, I've always associated any kind of waiting with death and decay.' Say it with me: 'It's still very raw.'

5. **Don't be fooled by trust exercises**: the trust exercise is designed to give you the false impression that you can trust people who shouldn't be trusted. If my experiences with drama and drama-folk have taught me anything, it is this: TRUST NO ONE. Just because someone is there to catch you when you fall backwards, doesn't mean they're not going to laugh about you later over Rioja and tapas.

Your drama tutor will tell you, 'Be fearless, let yourself go, open yourself up to the experience.' Your drama tutor is a prick. Keep your head down, do your time and get out as soon as you can.

# How to Clean a House

## By Vod

OK, so I'm gonna be telling you about cleaning houses. Or rather, cleaning your own student house. If you're planning to become some kind of professional house-cleaner then you're in the wrong place, mate. This isn't for you. Go get an NVQ in dusting or something.

All right, the rest of you – amateurs, foot soldiers, grunts, anyone who's ever picked up a broom and thought, Fuck this, put the broom down again and gone and spent the afternoon down the arcade trying to cash in on the fruities – listen up. I'm only going to say this once.

My main and most important cleaning tip is, obviously, DON'T. Don't do it. If you don't care about living in a little Martha-Stewart-Cath-Kidston-scented-candle-palace-of-rose-petals-up-on-Waltons-Mountain, then do not fucking get involved. Leave the cleaning to someone who cares about things being clean. You might, at some point, find yourself living with the sort of person who enjoys making a 'cleaning rota'. These people generally like to put everyone on the rota – they tend to talk all sorts of bullshit about 'fairness' and 'everyone pulling their weight'. Rota-makers often fancy themselves as quite 'good people', so I'd suggest playing the religion card to get yourself taken off the list. Hook up – or claim to hook up – with some sort of religion. You know, one of those really busy ones. One where you're up and down praying all day, or have to spend the mornings nose-down on a special rug, or need to go out knocking on doors in a suit till the cows come home. That way, when the little Cif-Nazi comes at you with the laminated Excel spreadsheet, you can just give it a quick, 'Nah, mate, sorry, can't do any of them times. Need to go down the prayer hall. Doing the dishes would be offensive to my religion.' This generally shuts them up, I find.

However, there might come a point in your life when you've got no choice but to pick up a cloth and get going. Perhaps you've had some kind of massive party and you're worried that your house will start oozing onto the street. Perhaps you've had the

environmental health on your back for a few months, and you're worried your mum might go mental if they put you back inside. Perhaps you've got a bit of a crime-scene-clear-up situation going on – hey, no, don't tell me. I'm not asking, don't wanna know. Anyway. There's a mess, and there's only you to deal with it. Here are my tips for dealing with it:

## Tip no. 1

Remember that a garden is basically a big bin, and so-called 'ponds' are ideal for the storage of liquid waste. Petrol floats, most bodily fluids sink. If you've got a lot of either then you might want to net any fish out and dump them in a bucket or something. Fish don't get on with petrol.

## Tip no. 2

If for whatever reason you need to set fire to a mattress, for God's sake don't do it on the roof. Onlookers'll think your house is on fire and they'll call the pigs, and you could find yourself down the station trying to chat your way out of an arson charge the night before your A-level politics exam. No, if it's really got to be got rid of, dig a hole in the garden or drag it out into the forest and bury it. The only way to safely burn a mattress is on the beach. Wait till low tide, drag it down to just a few feet above the water,  douse it in petrol, light a match then FUCKING RUN FOR YOUR LIFE. Don't worry about the Coastguard – they can pretty much always be bought off with real ale (barrels, not pints I'm afraid).

## Tip no. 3

Puddles look better than smears. That's just a basic art fact. If cleaning up a puddle's going to make a smear, leave the fucking puddle. Just leave it as it is.

On the subject of puddles, buy some cones. Like the ones hospital cleaners have – you know, those big yellow bastards with 'CAUTION WET FLOOR' written on them etc. And then just put the cones around the puddle. It'll look like you're planning on dealing with it later. You can nick the cones from an institution if you need to. It's worth a few hours hanging out down the council offices (they're generally quite low-security) to get your hands on a few. They're really handy and it can be quite a fun day out.

## Tip no. 4

Carpets are a waste of fucking time. Any twat who gets a carpet frankly deserves to have them thrown up on. However, if you do find yourself nose down on a Sunday morning trying to scrub a cum-stain off your Aunty Mabel's Axminster (for example) – do the following:

1. Apply all available brands of carpet cleaner. Use according to the instructions on the packet.
2. Apply baking soda to the stain and scrub with a little wire brush.
3. Apply fizzy water and salt, then scrub with a little wire brush.
4. Apply vodka, bit more with the little wire brush.
5. Apply vinegar. Blot. Scrub. Blot again. Bit more scrubbing.

None of this will make any difference at all to the carpet – carpet's fucked, mate; we all need to get over it and move on – but at least when the carpet owner gets all up in your face about it you can say, 'Look, mate, did the vinegar, did the Vanish, did the fucking little wire brush. Did all I could. It's over. Let's go kill this pain with a bottle of voddy.

## Tip no. 5

Walls and ceilings. It's very, very easy to chuck stuff up a wall or ceiling. Believe me, I know. I've been there. One over-enthusiastic gesture with a pint of cider and black in your mitt and – boom – bye bye chandelier. And then you're lumbered with the job of getting up on a chair with a cloth on a stick, endlessly bloody faffing around, with all your mates standing hurling abuse at you and poking your arse with a fork. Manky.

So I've got two tips for walls and ceilings. Firstly, blame a baby. This works better for walls than ceilings, admittedly, as it's a pretty rare baby who can catapult a mouthful of Ribena right up in the sky (sounds a bit *Exorcist* or *Omen* if we're honest – eurgh!). Anyway, yeah, if it's the wall – preferably the lower half of the wall – blame a baby: 'The baby did it when your back was turned.' If some family are in your home this'll make the parents feel so guilty that they're bound to offer you some sort of small cash handout for the cleaning, which you can then accept, before not doing any cleaning and spending the cash however you please. Brilliant.

Secondly – and this works best for those tough ceiling stains – find a way to make sure people look at the floor. Dunno how, maybe a rug or a rabbit in a cage or some kind of floor art or something? I've never actually tried this one – I've only just thought of it – but it sounds like the sort of thing one of those interior-decorator home-improvements wankers might suggest, doesn't it?

## Tip no. 6

OK, we're nearly done. But tips wouldn't be complete without a quick word about . . . OVEN CLEANING. Oh yeah. Oven cleaning is the only kind of cleaning I'd advocate volunteering for, or doing on a regular basis. Oven cleaning is basically as close as a law-abiding civilian can come to the experience of large-scale chemical warfare. It's mental. Seriously. You can buy, like, a special outfit for doing it in. And the shit you've gotta do it with is hardcore. Seriously. Mr Muscle Oven is only two steps down from what the Soviets kept in a bunker during the Cold War. One whiff of that and you're off your nut for a week, especially if you shut all the windows, put earplugs up your nose, deep breath, open wide and

**THE REMAINDER OF THIS ARTICLE HAS BEEN DELETED IN THE INTERESTS OF READER SAFETY.**

# Howard's Flowchart 2:
## Schematic for phoning home

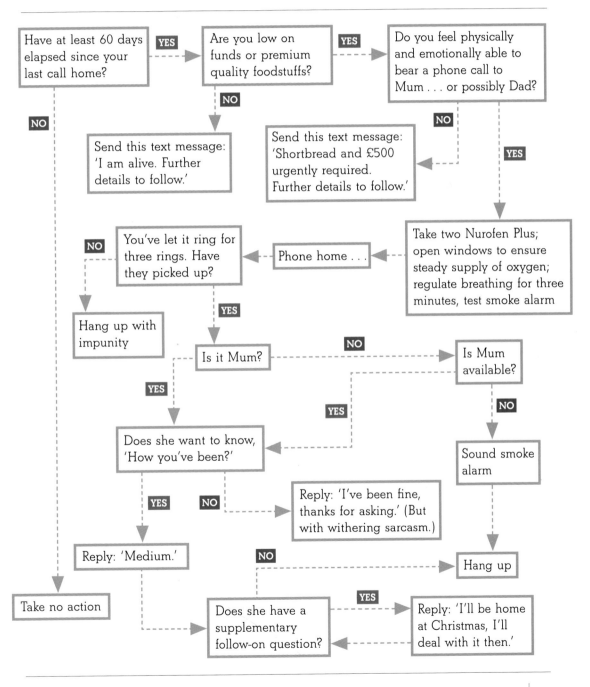

Have at least 60 days elapsed since your last call home? **YES** → Are you low on funds or premium quality foodstuffs? **YES** → Do you feel physically and emotionally able to bear a phone call to Mum . . . or possibly Dad?

**NO**

**NO** → Send this text message: 'I am alive. Further details to follow.'

**NO** → Send this text message: 'Shortbread and £500 urgently required. Further details to follow.'

**YES** → Take two Nurofen Plus; open windows to ensure steady supply of oxygen; regulate breathing for three minutes, test smoke alarm

You've let it ring for three rings. Have they picked up? ← Phone home . . . ← 

**NO** → Hang up with impunity

**YES** → Is it Mum? **NO** → Is Mum available?

**YES** → Does she want to know, 'How you've been?'

**NO** → Sound smoke alarm

Does she want to know, 'How you've been?' **NO** → Reply: 'I've been fine, thanks for asking.' (But with withering sarcasm.)

**YES** → Reply: 'Medium.'

Take no action

Does she have a supplementary follow-on question? **YES** → Reply: 'I'll be home at Christmas, I'll deal with it then.'

**NO** → Hang up

# NEW HOUSEMATE GUIDELINES FOR 28 HARTNELL ROAD

## Formulated and compiled by Howard (you're welcome)

Greetings reader(s). It appears that for some reason you have insisted on moving into this house. Congratulations, I guess.

Now that the obligatory congratulations are out of the way, please take note of the following rules, policies, customs, traditions and myths you must respect for the duration of your stay.

Think of this as a 'Boy Scouts Handbook' for surviving in the house, except with less information about knots and your duties as an obedient citizen–soldier. If you need it, I will be able to give you some advice on camouflaging yourself for safety reasons.

*If you are reading this document but, for whatever reason, do not actually live at 28 Hartnell, please ignore the information about where we keep our spare key.*

1. There is a spare key hidden underneath an overturned pot plant next to the front door.

   i. Please do not make copies of the key. For three months the boyfriend of one of the previous tenants used to let himself in to use our bath because he didn't have a tub at his new place. It was annoying.

2. The bins are collected on Thursday mornings.

   i. If you talk to 'Whiz' – the tall bloke with a Rastafarian Bart Simpson tattoo – he will let you know if he has collected anything good that he is willing to sell (e.g., our previous microwave or our current shower head).

3. There is a first-aid kit in the kitchen, but please be aware that it is mostly filled with old cigarette lighters, loose change and Haribo.

4. My room is ALWAYS off limits.

   i. If you need something from me, please slide a note under the door.

   ii. Give your problem an impartial rating from 1–10, with 1 being the least serious (e.g., a social problem with a fellow housemate) and 10 being the most serious (e.g., nuclear attack).

5. If you get sick, please do the decent thing and stay in your room until you feel better and are no longer contagious.

    i. If the illness is bad enough that you need to go to the doctor, maybe it's your body's way of telling you it's time to give up.

6. In the event of a *28 Days Later*-style viral outbreak, the room under the stairs can/will be used as a panic room.

    i. There is only enough space for me and one other person.

    ii. I will be observing all housemates throughout the year to decide who among you would be most valuable in a post-apocalyptic world.

7. The Wi-Fi password is in my bedroom. If you'd like to log on to the internet let me know (see rule 4ii).

8. The brown-green stain on the living-room carpet has been there since my first week in the house.

    i. I've got a small prize (bacon) for anybody who can guess what originally caused the stain (clue: it's not a food, but you can eat it if necessary).

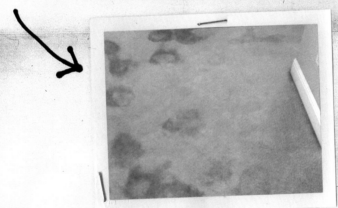

9. There is a homeless guy who walks past the house everyday around 3 p.m. He has a dog and is usually fine, but I have refined specific ways to deal with him should he engage you:

    i. Safe topics of discussion include: the weather, The Stone Roses (and to a lesser extent the Happy Mondays), full English breakfasts.

    ii. Do NOT get involved in conversations about: immigration, the Bible, who really killed Haile Selassie.

10. Do not call the landlord under any circumstances.

# HOWARD'S GOOD & BAD LIST

It is my humble assertion that everything in this world can be divided into one of two sub-categories: GOOD and BAD. I am currently engaged in a practical exercise to arrange everything in the known world into a definitive list. I will post the finished article online as a reference tool; a bit like Wikipedia, the difference being this actually _means_ something. Below is a mere excerpt of my ongoing research.

| GOOD | BAD |
|------|-----|
| SLIPPERS | SLIP-ONS |
| QUARTZ DIORITE | QUARTZ MONZONITE |
| SNORKELLING | SCUBA DIVING |
| FIG ROLLS | (See biscuit appendices) |
| LEICESTERSHIRE | SURREY |
| Time (The concept) | Time (the Manchester night club) |
| K2 (the mountain) | K2 (the Manchester night club) |
| "HUNGER" (the film) | HUNGER (the sensation) |
| SHROVE TUESDAY | ASH WEDNESDAY |
| CHEESE | PINEAPPLE |
| YIN | YANG |
| YANG | YIN |
| QUAVERS | MINI-CHEDDARS |
| ABSEILING | PAINTBALL |
| AA BATTERIES | AAA BATTERIES |
| THE DUKE OF EDINBURGH AWARDS | THE DUKE OF EDINBURGH |
| SHOWERS | BATHS |
| LYNX "INSTINCT" | LYNX 'AFRICA THROUGH VOODOO' |
| DRUM, BASS | DRUM & BASS |

Contd: ⟶

# GOOD | BAD

→ Contd. from previous page

**LITERATURE SECTION**

| GOOD | BAD |
|---|---|
| NORMAL BOOKS | THE LORD OF THE RINGS: The fellowship of the Ring |
| NON ELF-BASED BOOKS | THE LORD OF THE RINGS: The Two Towers |
| BOOKS ABOUT REAL PEOPLE | THE LORD OF THE RINGS: The Return of the King |
| SHORT, FACTUAL BOOKS | THE HOBBIT |
| HIGH FIDELITY | THE LOW AND MEDIUM FIDELITIES |
| RGB | CMYK |
| MUM | DAD |
| WHITE CHOCOLATE | WHITE SUPREMACY |
| ~~APPLE~~ | ~~APPLE~~ |
| ~~HEWLETT PACKARD~~ | |
| HEWLETT | PACKARD |
| NEPTUNE | VENUS (up itself) |
| PLUTO | SATURN (showy) |
| EARTH | MARS (over-rated) |
| DAVID SUCHET | DAVID KORESH |
| PLAIN, INOFFENSIVE SPECTACLES | 'JAZZY', 'FUNKY' SPECTACLES |
| .Jpeg | .tiff |
| BUFFET ETIQUETTE | BUFFET ANARCHY (sweet/savoury on same plate) |
| SHIRTS ON | 'GOING SKINS' |
| COUSIN ADAM | (see Extended family appendices) |
| RHOMBUS | TRAPEZOID |
| SOLO TAPAS | GROUP TAPAS (high potential for split-bill confusion) |
| SQUARE SIDEBURNS | POINTED SIDEBURNS |
| PLANTS | PETS |
| PAPERCLIPS | UNCLIPPED PAPERS |
| HIKING | MEANDERING |
| COMPLIANT SEX-DROIDS | AGGRESSIVELY INTELLIGENT ANTI-HUMAN CYBORGS |
| HOVERCRAFTS | HYDROFOILS |
| BOSCH POWER TOOLS | OTHER, INFERIOR POWER TOOLS |
| BRIAN HOWARTH? | BRIAN HOWARTH? |

# How to Facilitate a Clean Mugging
## A Mugee's Guide

**By Howard MacCallum**

People are always asking me, 'Howard, what can I do as an individual to oil the wheels of the violent robbery process? What can I do to facilitate a clean mugging?' First off, I ask them to stand me a nice cold pint of Boddingtons. Then, once we've found a suitably cosy seat in front of the roaring hearth, this is what I tell them.

## 1. Embrace it

There are only three certainties in this life: death, taxes, and that you'll get mugged an average of 4.5 times per annum. The sooner you stop trying to avoid being robbed with menaces and start accepting that it's going to happen to you a lot more often than you would ideally like, the better. If it helps, try not to think of it as an act of criminality but more as a kind of involuntary donation towards a benevolent fund set up for the benefit of under-educated thugs and bullies. It sure works for me.

**FIGURE.01**

Average per capita annual muggings (4.5)

## 2. Learn the ABCs of an efficient mugging

**A**lways

**B**e

**C**ompliant

It's important to know your role in the process. The mugger's role is to be aggressive and physically intimidating. Your role is to hand over your items in the most time-efficient manner possible. Everyone has their own little routine, here's mine: head down; hand over wallet; hand over phone; turn out pockets; step aside to allow easy exit route. If you're bespectacled, as I am, you might like to remove your glasses to establish to your assailant that you'll be unable to identify them later in a line-up. For the record, my quickest mugging from first contact to final handover was seven seconds. Traumatic, sure, but oddly gratifying.

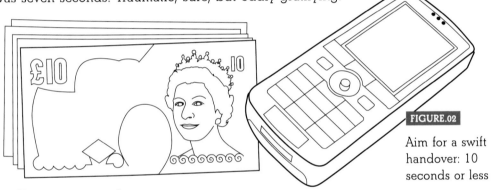

FIGURE.02

Aim for a swift handover: 10 seconds or less

## 3. Be prepared

I was recently frogmarched to a cash machine in Angel Square only to discover that the daily withdrawal allowance on my new savings account was a paltry £100. The result? One unhappy mugger and a well-deserved punch in the guts for Mr H. MacCallum! With this in mind, think about speaking to your bank about increasing your daily withdrawal allowance to a hearty, no-quibble £250.

(Of course, this is just the 'daily' allowance. In the circumstance outlined above, I offered to sleep on the mugger's sofa so we could wake up early the following morning to withdraw a second amount. He politely declined.)

## 4. Check your emotions in at the door

Remember, muggers are like spiders – they're just as scared of you as you are of them. Any sudden shifts in mood are liable to spook them. Be stoic. There'll be plenty of time for crying later, believe you me!

## 5. Go the extra mile

You've emptied your wallet, you've maxed out your debit cards, and yet still that greedy little mugger seems hungry for more. There's no harm in offering up a watch, a pair of trainers, a piece of jewellery. It's these small personal touches that will endear you to the mugger, helping to forge an emotional bond that'll prevent them from ever targeting you again. (Of course, there is a counter-argument that suggests that giving your mugger £70 in cash, a Casio G-Shock, a pair of Nike Air Max 95s and a 9ct gold necklace will positively encourage him to return for subsequent muggings. My research on this thus far has been inconclusive.)

FIGURE.03

Why not offer him your Casio G-Shock?

## 6. Finally, keep mum!

There's a reason why you never hear people talking about how they've been mugged at least four times a year every year for the last three years – because no one wants to bloody hear it! However much you may feel tempted to go home in the aftermath of an unusually brutal attack and waffle on about the feelings of dread and terror you're starting to experience every time you leave the house, save it. In my experience, any negative emotions such as these are best bottled up. Eventually, you'll find yourself exploding into sudden bursts of angry screaming with less and less frequency.

Until, of course . . .

'Excuse me, mate, have you got the time?'
WALLOP!

FIGURE.04

Silence is golden . . .

# The Substance Abuse Chart!

So everyone knows students are wild party animals who will try anything just to get their kicks! I thought it might be fun to do a little survey of 'the housemates' and see who's tried what, and what they thought. Don't try this at home, kids! Make sure you go out to P–A–R–T–Y!

| Housemate |
| --- |
| HOWARD |
| KINGSLEY |
| JP |
| OREGON |
| JOSIE |
| VOD |

| Booze | Fags | Marijuana |
|---|---|---|
| Interesting taste, noticeable side-effects negligible. Apparently, I am immune. | Pointless. | Immune. Appears to make others ravenous, irritating and stupid. |
| 0% - - - - - - - -> 100% | 0% - - - - - - - -> 100% | 0% - - - - - - - -> 100% |
| I'm a beer man. | Only after the beer, man! | Beer then wine, you'll feel fine. Beer then mega-bong hit, you'll feel shit. |
| 0% - - - - - - - -> 100% | 0% - - - - - - - -> 100% | 0% - - - - - - - -> 100% |
| JP loves a JD. | Hell yes. Give me 40 a day. I'm not afraid. | Skunk (Cheese fave), Thai weed, Hash, Black – it's all good. |
| 0% - - - - - - - -> 100% | 0% - - - - - - - -> 100% | 0% - - - - - - - -> 100% |
| Been drinking since I was 10. | Been smoking since I was 11. | Yup. Since I was 12. Got SUCH a bad memory now. Lolz! |
| 0% - - - - - - - -> 100% | 0% - - - - - - - -> 100% | 0% - - - - - - - -> 100% |
| Love it! Favourite is . . . pina colada. Mmm! | Um. Lung cancer? | Can give you serious mental health problems and affect motivation. |
| 0% - - - - - - - -> 100% | 0% - - - - - - - -> 100% | 0% - - - - - - - -> 100% |
| 8/10 – hangovers can be bad. | 10/10 – smoke menthols for a healthier choice. | 9/10 – similar to smoking but better for you and chills you out. |
| 0% - - - - - - - -> 100% | 0% - - - - - - - -> 100% | 0% - - - - - - - -> 100% |

|  | Speed | Ecstasy/MDMA | Cocaine |
|---|---|---|---|
| **HOWARD** | 1 x accidental usage. Impairs flavour of tea. Induces *extreme* paranoia, but resulted in incredibly well-filed hard drive.<br><br>0% ------------▶ 100% | I have no desire to 'love' everyone. Or dance.<br><br>0% ------------▶ 100% | 3 x experimental use. Side-effects included diarrhoea (verbal and actual).<br><br>0% ------------▶ 100% |
| **KINGSLEY** | Nope.<br><br>0% ------------▶ 100% | No.<br><br>0% ------------▶ 100% | No thanks.<br><br>0% ------------▶ 100% |
| **JP** | Dirty come-downs, no ta. Why take speed when you could take . . .<br><br>0% ------------▶ 100% | . . . Ecstasy! YES! PARTY ON wid da Love Machine.<br><br>0% ------------▶ 100% | The gentleman's drug. Snort it UP.<br><br>0% ------------▶ 100% |
| **OREGON** | Oh god. SO much speed at school. So much! Too much to repeat it ever again.<br><br>0% ------------▶ 100% | Yes & yes. Not sure if still would, since quality is so reduced now.<br><br>0% ------------▶ 100% | Obviously had a 'bit of a coke problem' when I was 15? So can't really do it now.<br><br>0% ------------▶ 100% |
| **JOSIE** | Puts you at risk of heart attack, people. Come on!<br><br>0% ------------▶ 100% | Don't you remember the girl who DIED from not drinking enough water?<br><br>0% ------------▶ 100% | Addictive, cut with rat poison, turns you into a fucking wanker.<br><br>0% ------------▶ 100% |
| **VOD** | 5/10 – makes me feel a bit mental.<br><br>0% ------------▶ 100% | 9/10 – good times almost every time, tho not what it used to be.<br><br>0% ------------▶ 100% | 7/10 – expensive, effects short-lived.<br><br>0% ------------▶ 100% |

| LSD ● | Heroin ● | Other |
|---|---|---|
| Claims that it allows one to peer into your very essence means it is not suitable for me. <br><br> 0% - - - - - - → 100% | N/A. <br><br> 0% - - - - - - → 100% | Never eat a Berocca without first dissolving it in water. |
| Again, no. <br><br> 0% - - - - - - → 100% | Next! <br><br> 0% - - - - - - → 100% | If I have to pick one, it would be Piriton. |
| Not yet. The gap in my education. <br><br> 0% - - - - - - → 100% | I totes would, but only if it was Victorian times. <br><br> 0% - - - - - - → 100% | Tippex: the schoolboy staple. |
| Yawn. Yeah, it doesn't really 'do it' for me any more. <br><br> 0% - - - - - - → 100% | The stuff in Thailand is WAY better than over here. <br><br> 0% - - - - - - → 100% | OK, so *maybe* crack. A couple of times. Don't tell anyone! |
| Don't you remember the guy who had horrible flashbacks FOR LIFE? <br><br> 0% - - - - - - → 100% | Immediately addictive and highly dangerous. DRUGS KILL! <br><br> 0% - - - - - - → 100% | Ibuprofen is really good for period pain. |
| 8/10 – turns all TV into a cartoon! Yes! <br><br> 0% - - - - - - → 100% | NEVER! Fuck that shit, I'm no junkie. <br><br> 0% - - - - - - → 100% | Temazepam, ketamine, properidine, diazepam, rohypnol, PCP, codeine, etc. |

## 2 | CONFIDENTIAL | Student sexual health questionnaire

**Name:** (you do not have to complete this)

Howard

**Indicate your gender:**

male

**Indicate your age:**

24

**Are you sexually active?** OFFline no. But I run a number of online avatars, three of whom could currently be classed as "active".

**Do you use contraception every time you have sex?**

I have had sex five times, and on three of those occasions some form of contraception was used. On the remaining two occasions the lady in question was too old to bear children.
    None of my avatars use contraception, as we mate with the intention of breeding.

**Indicate which form of contraception you use?**

One condom (me), one contraceptive coil (her), one pill (her); and actually the older lady did have a go with one of those female condom things, which look like a tubular shower cap, but we didn't use it in the end as it rustled very loudly.

**Where do you purchase your contraception**

I generally leave the ladies to take care of that.

**3**

Have you recently suffered from any of the following sexually transmitted diseases that you are aware of?

| HIV / AIDS | Syphillis | Gonorrhea | Herpes |
|---|---|---|---|
| No | YES | No | No |

| Chlamydia | Hepatitis B or C | Other (please specify) |
|---|---|---|
| No | No | Athlete's Foot. |

Have you recently had unprotected oral or anal sex?

Offline, no.

Where do you get most of your information on sexual health?

Manga cartoons and those leaflets you get in boxes of tampons (the diagram is generally very helpful).

Would you say you are well informed about your sexual health?

No. Absolutely not. I am a danger to myself and others.

Do you have any other comments?

I'm not sure about the syphilis, but I'd appreciate a check-up.

## 2 CONFIDENTIAL Student sexual health questionnaire

**Name:** (you do not have to complete this)

Vod

**Indicate your gender:**

Female. Thanks.

**Indicate your age:**

18 - 25

**Are you sexually active?**

When the mood takes me

**Do you use contraception every time you have sex?**

Yeah, mostly. Unless we're too wasted to sort it out. These really are fucking annoying questions.

**Indicate which form of contraception you use?**

Your Mum's face

**Where do you purchase your contraception**

I got your Mum's face from Lidl

*Unless it'll get me out of exams, in which case it's a big fat YES.

## 3

**Have you recently suffered from any of the following sexually transmitted diseases that you are aware of?**

**I'm fucking rotten with it. About three weeks away from the locked-in-an-attic-screaming-my-tits-off stage

| HIV / AIDS | Syphilis | Gonorrhea | Herpes |
|---|---|---|---|
| No * | Yep ** | Yeah | Wear it as a badge of honour Yep. |

| Chlamydia | Hepatitis B or C | Other (please specify) |
|---|---|---|
| Doesn't everyone have this? | Yeah *** | Um... scabies? Yeah, why not. Scabies |

**Have you recently had unprotected oral or anal sex?**

Yeah, on your Mum's sofa

**Where do you get most of your information on sexual health?**

Your Mum.

**Would you say you are well informed about your sexual health?**

Not as well informed as your Mum.

**Do you have any other comments?**

I was lying about all them sex diseases. Obviously, I am as clean as a whistle. UNLIKE YOUR MUM.

***I got it from wanking off a tramp. Happy?

## 2 CONFIDENTIAL Student sexual health questionnaire

**Name:** (you do not have to complete this)

Oregon

**Indicate your gender:**

Female

**Indicate your age:**

19

**Are you sexually active?**

YES

**Do you use contraception every time you have sex?**

Yes, definitely

**Indicate which form of contraception you use?**

I've probably used them all at different times in my sexual career (I'm very experienced for someone my age). I like to take responsibility for contraception, as a lot of older men don't enjoy using condoms (I've been with a number of older men)

**Where do you purchase your contraception**

When I was on my gap year I brought a lot with me from the UK- I was travelling to some pretty remote, sexually spontaneous places, you see, and it was vital that I felt free to experience all the world has to offer.

**3**

Have you recently suffered from any of the following sexually transmitted diseases that you are aware of?

| HIV / AIDS NO But I did encounter some AIDS victims on my gap yr & was profoundly moved by the experience | Syphilis NO | Gonorrhea NO | Herpes NO |
|---|---|---|---|
| Chlamydia NO (though – can you catch it from toilet seats? They say you can't, but you must be able to a bit) | Hepatitis B or C NO | Other (please specify) I'd really welcome some clarity on the whole toilet-seat thing | |

Have you recently had unprotected oral or anal sex?

The former, yes. The latter, absolutely not (though he did sort of 'probe' it with a finger – does that count?)

Where do you get most of your information on sexual health?

My various lovers

Would you say you are well informed about your sexual health?

For someone of my age, extraordinarily well informed.

Do you have any other comments?

Is this going to be sent out to our parents?

Friday, 4 November

Am going to offer to break K's virginity. Vod and Oregon think is wise idea, and I am inclined to think they are right.

Am going to try and raise subject with K tomorrow, see what he says. Not sure how to do this. Might tell him about my friend Matthew Mullins who never even wanked (his mum told him the Virgin Mary was watching) and then one day his foreskin grew over his jizz-hole and closed it up. Possibly also drop hints about what a great shag I am, though not sure that's good idea. Don't want to intimidate him with sexual prowess.

Will definitely decide to break up with Dave before do this, as is most unfair otherwise.


Saturday, 5 November

KINGSLEY SAID YES!!!!!

Remember, remember the fifth of November. OH. MY. GOD! Will there be FIREWORKS????

Must definitely break up with Dave now. Shit!

Am going to make post-it flow chart to decide on best way.

I keep thinking to myself, Am I being callous? Is this wrong? Am I a BAD PERSON? And then I think, but no! I am young! I am free! If I don't do this sort of crazy thing at university then I will end up doing it when I am a mother, like Rhiannon's mum who had a crisis when she hit 40 and ran off with the hairdresser. If I don't do this now, I will end up being a lesbian in Llandudno!

I refuse to feel bad!

I'm going to shag K on Thursday... and I can't wait!

Sunday 6th November

Am really worried K will have tiny penis.

Have been studying his hands, they are of average size. Good sign?

Feel it is likely will still love him even if he has tiny penis, but will be disappointed. For him as much as my self. Always think how bad must be for man to have tiny penis. Like having giant nose, only worse, because secret.

Wonder if that is why he is virgin?


Sunday 20th November

Sorry haven't written for ages. Events have got the better of me.

Have been on political march! V exciting! Actually got KETTLED - made me feel like a real activist! Something to tell grandchildren (hello, grandchildren - if you are reading this!).

Other stuff too. But can't be bothered to write it all now. V tired and hungover. Might go and cry in my bed for a bit.

## Monday 21st November

Not sure uni is quite working out the way I'd planned. To recap, the following things have happened:

1. Shagged Kingsley, turned out he wasn't even a virgin. LIAR!
2. Meant to break up with Dave, but of course he INTERRUPTED ME on the phone to tell me it was his nan's birthday. So instead accidentally ended up getting engaged to Dave.
3. Dave came down for a surprise visit and, through no fault of mine, ended up finding out about Kingsley and JP. Really unfortunate as fair enough to be upset about K, but JP was very much an accident and blip and I shouldn't be held accountable for that as was v drunk and regretted it immediately.
4. Dave broke up with me!!! So much for in sickness and in health and all that bullshit. It's like Vod says, if he called off the wedding just because I shagged two of my housemates, how would he have coped with a lifetime of being married??? BETTER OFF OUT OF IT.

On the other hand, my course is going quite well. Hopefully one day when I am a rich and famous dentist I will look back on all this and chortle merrily at my younger self while sitting on my yacht.

Sunday 10th December

Nearly the end of term already! Can't believe it. Gone so fast and so much has happened!

Dave said when I went to uni I would change, and I swore that wouldn't happen... but feel like am changing / have changed. Might make list to see...

List of changes:
1. Can drink wine without vomiting.[1]
2. Am single.
3. In love with boy with hairless chest who pretended to be virgin.
4. Have had sex with two more boys (total six boys, seems loads more than previous four — is in fact NEARLY 10 - eek!)[2]
5. Am officially becoming dentist.
6. Know new bus routes.
7. Cooking and washing for self 100% of time instead of just when Mum is working late and tired.
8. Only do laundry every three weeks.
9. Wear socks two days in a row minimum.
10. Have friends who are not Welsh.
11. Have friend who is not white![3]

However:
1. Hair the same.
2. Face the same.
3. Weight the same (despite additional drinking and sitting around — think anxiety of man situation has kept off those extra pounds).
4. Still feel like the same person inside, sort of...
Seems like maybe I've changed a bit.

Sunday 31st December

Resolutions for next term:

1. Be teetotal.
2. Be celibate.
3. Do my washing more often.
4. Make more friends outside the house.
5. Study harder.
6. Go to 100% of lectures, even the non-compulsory ones.
7. Join three more societies.
8. Jog every morning.
9. Eat more vegetables.
10. Stop secretly obsessing about Kingsley.

---

FOOTNOTES

1. Clarification: can drink two bottles of red wine before vomiting becomes an inevitability (instead of one sip as previously).

2. Must stop shagging now till third year. Well-known fact that any girl whose number is into double figures before they are 21 is definitely a slag. Still have two and a half years to go and am already at six!

3. It doesn't need to be said that I am obviously fine with this. Welsh people not racist except against English people. Apart from Racist Ron, my dad's friend who is actually racist and went to a convention in Bradford and collects Nazi memorabilia. NB: is only Dad's friend because of rugby tickets. Dad not actually in favour of Nazi memorabilia. In fact, Nazi memorabilia is only a rumour. Might not even be true. Ron definitely is racist, though, and does ~~not~~ look like kind of person with secret Gestapo uniform collection (moustache like a pervert).

# Part Two

# Out of the Lecture Hall

# VODZ
AUTHENTIC STREETWEAR / violetnordstrom666@hotmail.com

WAR
STORIES

spitter
VODZ

psycho spice

VODZ

# A Beginner's Guide to 'Westly Fours'

## By Jonathan 'JP' Pembersley

Besides the fucking lush on-site laundry service, the best thing about going to Stowe is that you become one of the chosen few who gets to play the legendary, elite sport of Westly Fours.

Westly Fours (or 'Foursies') basically combines the power and aggression of rugby, the precision and accuracy of golf and some of the rules of chess to make the fastest, most kick-arse sport ever played! Seriously, it makes Formula One look like fucking musical chairs.

I was pretty much consistently the best player in my age range, and I've got the school newspaper match reports to prove it! The problem is, none of the plebs up here in Manchester have ever even heard of it, so I thought I'd spread the word and hopefully get a few games going.

I've jotted down a bit of background info and the rules for all you novice mofos – I'm thinking if enough people get on board then maybe, come summertime, we can set up a few teams (maybe get a small league going?).

Also, if we sort this out quickly we might be able to get our hands on some sweet university funding. No offence to the university women's rugby team, but if those 'girls' get money to buy gum shields and protective bras, then we should definitely be eligible for some of that dollar.

## Brief history

Nobody knows the exact origins of Westly Fours, but the most widely accepted story is that it was invented by Arnold Westly, a local bellows-maker and philanthropist who lived next door to the Stowe grounds.

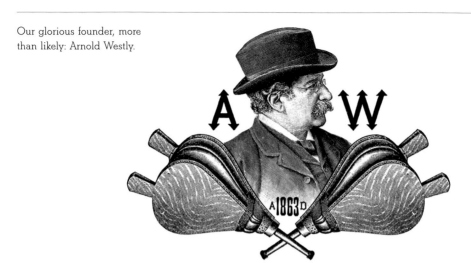

Our glorious founder, more than likely: Arnold Westly.

He thought that young boys weren't challenged enough (either physically or mentally) by the popular sports of the day, so he arranged to come into the school five times a week and teach a new game he had developed with his second wife. The sport was pretty much a success straight away, and since then we've played inter-house competitions every three months.

## Rules

Rumour has it that only two people have copies of the full Westly Fours rulebook, the current head boy at Stowe and the Duke of Edinburgh[1], but it's honestly really simple. Tom Gelby was wicked at it and he took his trousers all the way off to piss in urinals until he was 13, so I'm sure anyone can pick it up.

You need:

- An octagonal pitch (or 'Planter') with two nets at either end. The pitch is about the size of a tennis court and ideally the grass should be very long (to help prevent injuries).

- Each player has a long stick (or 'Skipper'), which is basically like a golf club with a solid, wooden ping-pong bat tied where the handle should be.

A 'skipper' from antiquity

- A hollow ball (or 'Blondie'). It's roughly the size of one and a half satsumas and is covered in moleskin. It's not unusual for the ball to travel at up to 150 mph.

---

1. Apparently they're not allowed to fly on the same plane – like the American President and Vice President, or the two guys who know the real recipe to Coca-Cola.

- Two teams of IV, X or XI (depending on how many people want to play).

The object of the game is to get the ball into the other team's net *by any means necessary*[2].

- You can score a point either by getting the ball into the net or by tackling the other team's captain (or 'Fluffer'[3]).

- It's full contact – tackling between boys is allowed and actively encouraged.

Teams of 4, 10 and 11 can participate. Probably 12 if you fancy it.

- You are NOT allowed to run when you have the ball in your third of the pitch OR the opponents' third of the pitch, but you ARE allowed to run if either you OR your opponent are in the middle third of the pitch, OR if you are injured.

- You can either paddle the ball to a team-mate (or 'Arnold'), or put the ball on the pitch and strike for goal.

- Girls and Irish people aren't allowed to play.

- All games are played to 17 and there's no time limit.

- For some reason, after the game, the losing team (or 'Slugs') has to empty a bottle of port onto the pitch while singing the traditional loser chant (or 'Slug Song'):

    *The good old boys have met, and done their very best.*
    *But a ho-ho-ho and rin-tin-tin, we'll get that fluffer yet!*

- Foursies MUST NOT be played on Bastille Day.

So that's basically it, simple really. Check it out, get playing and hopefully see you on the octagon, bitches!

---

2. The game is pretty much safe and nobody has ever actually died during a match, although apparently one kid lost an eye in the 80s, but by all accounts he was a bit of a bell-end.

3. I know, but don't worry, the game was invented *before* porn so it's not weird.

# Jonathan Pembersley's University Guide to Hip Hop

## A Bluffer's Guide by an Expert

(Beware! I have put in some things that are wrong so that you won't be able to fool me if I ever meet you.)

## Snoop Dogg

The shizzle. Beware, the 'izzle' suffix should now only be used humorously. Nota bene, it is no longer associated with cool in any way and should not be attempted in earnest, especially in those vital first few hours at uni. It can be dropped with wryness, but never *sans* wryness.

Snoop is a great starter piece for any youngling wishing to establish hardcore credentials. Spinning Doggy-style is never a *faux pas* and is always appreciated in even the most real circumstances. Snoop's flow is excellent. His polysyllabic work could do with attention in certain areas, but his dope rating remains high.

# WU-TANG

## Wu-Tang Clan

For the novice, a quick recap: RZA, Ghostface, GZA, Raekwon, the late Ol' Dirty Bastard, Method Man, Masta Killah, Inspectah Deck and U-God are all in the Wu-Tang Clan. In fact, so many people are in the Wu-Tang Clan that my advice is that if you meet a gentleman in an urban setting who says he's in the Wu-Tang Clan, then at least entertain the possibility that he is, due to the fact there are so many people in the Wu-Tang Clan.

The Clan are a great starter group for you at uni. Put on *36 Chambers*, open a door and watch the blunt heads roll in looking for friendship and maybe more.

## Nas

I personally consider *Illmatic* to be the hip-hop bible. Nas's flow is faultless – full-bodied reality with after-notes of humanity. He is so good that initially some people find him boring.

Of course he has huge and historic beef with Jay-Z. My advice on this, as with so many of hip hop's various beefs – and this served me well at Stowe – was to NOT GET INVOLVED. These are serious players, and unless you're carrying an eight plus one or a nine gauge, why not back the flip off?

## The Notorious B.I.G.

Like Roald Dahl's BFG, Notorious B.I.G. seems initially frightening, due to the fact that he is dead yet still manages to keep up a hectic schedule of new releases.

His flow is well structured.

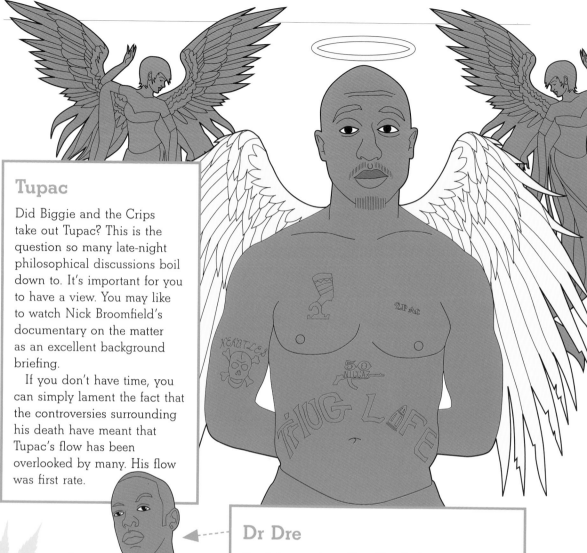

## Tupac

Did Biggie and the Crips take out Tupac? This is the question so many late-night philosophical discussions boil down to. It's important for you to have a view. You may like to watch Nick Broomfield's documentary on the matter as an excellent background briefing.

If you don't have time, you can simply lament the fact that the controversies surrounding his death have meant that Tupac's flow has been overlooked by many. His flow was first rate.

## Dr Dre

Don't forget about Dre. The Dr himself (who is also a qualified doctor) has warned against this error. Dre, of course, with Eazy-E and Ice Cube, formed the NWA in the nineteen hundred and eighties. If asked what the initials stand for in mixed company it is acceptable to nice it up by naming them Negroes with Attitude.

His flow is well structured. *The Chronic* is a masterpiece, and I seriously mean that. Possibly Dre's greatest achievement was his invention of Eminem at the 1997 Rap Olympics, where Slim Shady won, like Rebecca Adlington, in the freestyle section.

## 50 Cent

Also invented by Dr Dre at his beatsmith forge. His flow is good but by no means transcendent.

One of the main things the novice will notice about the Centipede is that his upper torso, of which he is rightly fond, appears to be forged from solid iron.

The novice should be aware that 50 Cent's central aim, according to his CD, was to 'get rich or die tryin''. This aim was also outlined in his film *Get Rich or Die Tryin'*. Happily, he has achieved the former, and in most fans' eyes has now retreated from The Game.

## Jay-Z

Has managed a feat unknown in human history – the first man to sell out *and* stay real at the same time. You can think about this for ever and it still doesn't make sense. It's like if Blair was also in Blur but nobody hated either of them.

He is, quite simply, the Jigga. Mr Beyoncé. He liked it – he put a ring on it.

*The Blueprint* is considered by many to be hip hop's bible. His flow is both smooth and strong, like an excellent cup of after-dinner coffee. But of rap!

## Grand Master Flash and the Furious Five

*The Message* is hip hop's bible. The original source others can return to and drink from the original flow.

## Public Enemy

*Yo! Bum Rush the Show* is the hip hop bible. The start of politically conscious rap that has done so much to influence me, and others like me, in our consciousness of black people and the things that have sometimes not gone their way, in their view.

Chuck D has excellent flow.

## Eminem

Until the invention of Eminem (formerly available as Slim Shady) most authorities were undecided on the question of whether a white man could ever imbibe sufficient quantities of reality to achieve lyrical flow.

It was felt that the black rapper had more innate advantages in achieving success, due to the increased likelihood of him having witnessed greater quantities of reality.

Eminem's tragic home life and successful drug use, however, has enabled him to generate flow. And although he has moaned on somewhat in recent years he is still worthy of a spin.

## A Tribe Called Quest

Some rap heads do not believe the Tribe and their flower-mates De La Soul and the Jungle Brothers to be real or street, due to their non-belief in the existence of bitches, dead presidents, nine gauges, pimps, hustlers, the chronic and all the other drugs and things that make up the rich landscape of hip hop.

This is not true. And I for one extend them the hand of friendship and issue this day an invitation for them to be accepted by all of us who are street and hype.

The Tribe, De La etc. and Drake are all excellent choices in mixed female company and will generally not offend. They do, however, believe in racial equality, so if this is likely to be contentious best to avoid the rap genre entirely and kick back with some non-political beats.

Peace Out!

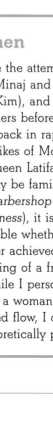

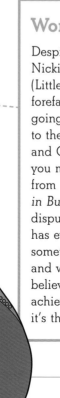

## Women

Despite the attempts of Nicki Minaj and Lil' Kim (Little Kim), and their forefathers before them, going back in rap prehistory to the likes of Monie Love and Queen Latifah (who you may be familiar with from *Barbershop 2: Back in Business*), it is still disputable whether a woman has ever achieved flow. I am something of a freethinker, and while I personally don't believe a woman has yet achieved flow, I do believe it's theoretically possible.

# The Josie Cycle I–III

A collection of poetry by Kingsley Owen

## I Memory foam

My mattress is not made of memory foam (Josie)
But if it was (Josie)
It would hold the memory of you.

I read a thing in the newspaper (Josie)
Which said that
Memory foam is dangerous.
Like, it's got some chemicals in it, which –
Despite new bedding laws –
Could prove harmful.

I don't know whether or not this is true (it can't be, surely).
But I do know that the memory of you –
So firmly imprinted on the foam of my mind –
Is deeply hazardous (Josie).

Because you've made a dent in my soul (Josie),
A dent, a trench, a quarry,
So much bigger and deeper than the dent in a mattress,
Left by even the hugest sleeping body.

And this dent – this dent in my soul – is a hazard.
No matter what the truth about the actual foam in mattresses is (again, I'm sure they wouldn't be allowed to sell them if they were dangerous)
The dent you leave in me (Josie)
Hurts me
Hurts me
Hurts me.

I hope that one day (Josie)
You and I will share a bed

And I hope that the bed will remember us.
Remember us, not as two separate gullies,
A yard of foam between us,
But as a unit. Our bodies intertwined,
Enmeshed, so as to form a single groove
Almost as big as a ditch (Josie).

And we will snuggle together in that gully-ditch,
You and I,
And make love.
And it will be better than anything you did with Dave.
Not to slag him off or anything (Josie).

Anyway. I press my face into my pillow
And I think of you.
Goodnight, my sweet (Josie)
And remember always,
That when we are together,
My bedding will remember you.

## II 'Munge'

I was vile about your munge today.
And yes – I know how that sounds.
I know that people might think of something rude
And laugh.
But I'm not even going to go there.
Because I have too much respect for you.

D'you hear that?
I. HAVE. TOO. MUCH. RESPECT. FOR. YOU.
Too much respect to make a joke about 'your munge',
Even though I hate you.
What does this mean?

Pain is what it means.
The sudden. Terrifying pain of realizing that
I am that munge.

I am that munge.
I am that munge.
I am that dreadful pot.
That bubbling hell of carbs.
My mind's a stew.
A thick stew, based upon the mushy beans of self-hatred
Fried atop the onions of despair
Flavoured with the back-of-the-cupboard cooking sherry of my youthful lust
And supported by the baked potato of my angry love for you.

A mess.
A putrid mess.
But through it all
Through all the vegetabloid muck
I glimpse the bright, shining studs, the sweetcorn of hope.
Little yellow stars burning bright through the silt-brown clouds of goo.
And for a moment, my munge-head clears.
And I can see the truth.

I sit and stare at the wall,
The paper-thin wall between us
(or it would be between us if you weren't still down in the kitchen).
And I think, again – I know
I Truly Am That Munge.

## III 'Dave'

Not much rhymes with 'Dave,' does it?
Slave. Grave. Shave. Cave. Behave.
Wave.
Nave.
Deprave.
No. Not much rhymes with 'Dave'.
Interesting.

Though if I were to choose one word,
One word which rhymes with 'Dave'.

I would choose 'deprave'.
Because I hear it, Dave.
I hear it through the wall, Dave.
I hear how hard you try,
How much you care,
And how little she enjoys it, Dave.
(I mean, when you're having sex.)
Yes, I hear you Dave.
Deprave.

If I were to choose another word
(a word which rhymes with Dave),
I'd probably choose 'grave'.
Because a grave is where I want to be,
Dave,
When you come round
And fix the telly
Which I cannot fix
Cannot fix
Cannot fix
For although your soul is rotten
You are handy with a spanner
And that makes me feel like a helpless, mewling boy-child,
Which makes me want to die
And go to my grave,
Dave.

I could go on.
I would go on.
But, thankfully – oh so thankfully –
Not much rhymes with Dave.

# BREACHING THE STORM WALL

Take one group of total strangers, put them in a shared house in the middle of an unfamiliar town, light the blue touch paper and stand well back . . .

This short story, written by Howard and retrieved from the James Bond fan-fiction network, gives an insight into the strange and intense feelings that can arise when you're forced to live 24/7 with a group of new people.

Oregon x

# Breaching the Storm Wall

A piece of erotic James Bond fan-fiction,
by Howard MacCallum

**'BOND ... JAMES BOND.'**

I pushed my glasses up my nose and took a long, cooling sip of my Yop strawberry yoghurt drink, then a female voice at the other end of the line said, 'The reservation is confirmed. We look forward to welcoming Mr Bond on the sixteenth.'

'Much obliged.'

My name was Howard MacCallum and I was a junior assistant travel coordinator at MI6. My job was to facilitate the travel arrangements and ongoing travel links for James Bond as he worked his way around the glamour spots of the world, fighting global terror.

And I loved every second of it ...

My remit was broad and logistically diverse, involving anything and everything from arranging visas to sourcing car hire; from winkling out the best deals on travel insurance to leaving the appropriate feedback on Trip Advisor. Managing the many travel incentive schemes on behalf of Mr Bond was a job in itself. (I'd recently spearheaded a company-wide initiative to bring all long-haul MI6 flights under the same airline. It had already borne fruit; to my satisfaction I had just used the air miles accrued to pay for a flight to Reykjavik, where I'm told Mr Bond drove a Lexus GX460 into a geyser and almost came to a sticky end, thanks to some particularly vicious Yakuza.)

But it wasn't only the intensely organizational aspect of my job that gave me great pleasure; there were other perks. Namely, the fact that I sat at the desk opposite hers.

Sabine ...

She was Dutch with a plain face. She had no distinguishing marks and her features were entirely symmetrical. She was medium build and wore neutral, inoffensive clothes. She was very punctual.

She was, in short, an absolute knockout ...

'Howard?' she said in her sexy monotone.

My heart pounded hard against the bony bars of its cage.

'Yes, Sabine?'

'I am having a problem with my computer. Ever since I updated to the newer version of OSX my Mac has started running really slowly. I am starting to wish I had never bothered to pay the £20.99 to upgrade to the Lion software, as I am told that the iCloud system isn't even that great. Are you able to help me?'

I took another long, hard plug on my strawberry Yop and wiped the sticky globules of pink yoghurty drink from the wiry bristles of my beard with the back of my hand.

'Yes, Sabine. I am able.'

I wheeled my chair over to her desk. As I sat in front of her MacBook Pro, I couldn't help but notice how clean the keyboard was. There were no crumbs between the keys, and it was blindingly obvious to me that she cleaned the screen with screen-wipes at least once a day.

'I see you take good care of your computer,' I noted, impressed.

'The keyboard is the number one source of germs in the office environment. It can contain more germs than a toilet.'

I laughed to myself. Who was this girl? So worldly, so wise, so hygienic ...

I began the process of verifying the disk permissions on her hard drive. We sat in silence, watching the progress bar gently ticking along ...

32% ... 33% ... 34% ...

I noticed for the first time that we were all alone in the office. It was mid-summer but the pollen count was low. The room temperature was 19 degrees exactly. The room was lit in such a way that we could see each other, but any physical defects would be hard to discern even at close range.

'Howard?'

'Yes, Sabine.'

57% ... 58% ... 59% ...

'I would like you to kiss me on the mouth.'

I swallowed hard.

62% ... 63% ... 64% ...

'Yes, Sabine.'

She turned and reached into her desk drawer and produced a bottle of generic supermarket mouthwash.

'Please ...'

She held out the bottle. I took it and swigged, feeling a sharp acidic tang as the antiseptic mouthwash collided with the Yop residue on my tongue.

78% ... 79% ... 80% ...

I ejected the mouthwash from my mouth into the soil of a nearby yucca plant.

Sabine pulled close to me and removed my glasses. We then inserted our tongues into each other's mouths, allowing the free exchange of saliva. Her spittle washed into my mouth, the foreign antibodies gushing over the storm wall of my lower teeth like Mexican immigrants swarming into the United States of America.

87% ... 88% ... 89% ...

Sabine pulled away.

'We cannot have full intercourse as I am in my menstrual cycle. Do you still want to continue kissing?'

'OK.'

92% ... 93% ... 94% ...

We continued kissing. This went on for about another 30 to 40 seconds.

Verifying disk permissions complete ...

Sabine pulled away for a second time.

'Thank you, Howard. I enjoyed the kissing and I hope that my MacBook Pro will now run more efficiently.'

'No problem. Next time you update OSX, you might want to try backing up your entire hard drive and then reinstalling everything.'

Sabine turned and continued typing. I wheeled myself back over to my desk. My hand trembled. I knew right then that I had just survived the single most intensely erotic experience of my 24 years.

The phone rang.

'Mr MacCallum, this is customer services from Avis Rental in Budapest. I'm just phoning to see whether you wanted to take out the optional windscreen insurance on your forthcoming booking.'

'How much is it?'

'There's a special offer on for this day only. It works out at just four euros.'

'OK then.'

'Let me just pull up the details of your booking. Please hold.'

I pushed my glasses up my nose and took a long, delicious gulp of my strawberry yoghurt drink.

Today was working out just fine ...

**A J.P. FILMS PRODUCTION**

**Bunce**

COZ SOME GEEZERS DIDN'T OUGHTA BE MESSED WIV...

18

University life isn't all curriculum, curriculum, curriculum. In the downtime between essay crises and exam all-nighters, you'll have plenty of space for self-exploration, self-expression and flights of creative fancy. JP spent his reading week last term writing his first ever feature-length screenplay. Apparently he's already got £50,000 of investment lined up from his friends back in Stowe . . .

*Oregon x*

Oregon Shawcross

# BUNCE

A Jonathan Pembersley film. Written, created and devised by
Jonathan Pembersley. All rights reserved Jonathan Pembersley.
Courtesy of JP-ictures and Pembersley Holdings, in association
with Nuff Respeck Films. Any resemblance to any persons living or
dead is entirely coincidental. (The character 'Rodger Pembersley'
is loosely based on my dad, Rodger Pembersley.)

EXTERIOR. LONDON - DAY

We're watching the most fucking incredible shot over the whole
of London while listening to the most amazing tune you've ever
heard in your life. We fly over Big Ben, through the London Eye,
and past the Gherkin, where we see a load of fuckwit suits, and
keep going until we get to the East End.

The people here in the East End somehow look more real than
the fuckwits we saw a minute ago. These are real, proper,
actual people. They're bloody poor and they're more or less all
criminals to one degree or another, but they're good, honest
(well, not honest) people - of all colours.

We push in on an East End pub. It's probably that one the Krays
used to work in. Inside the pub, at their regular table in
the corner, sit four of the hardest bastards in Great Britain.
They're playing poker and their names are:

BANGERS - a 31-year-old jack-the-lad. He's a bit like
Danny Dyer's character in The Football Factory, crossed with
Danny Dyer's character in The Business, but with the edge of
Danny Dyer's character in Outlaw. He's played by James McAvoy.

FRANKIE THE SNAKE - a 40-year-old psycho, alcoholic and fucking
liability. They call him Frankie the Snake because he's always
cheating at poker. And also because he's permanently got a snake
around his neck.

TOMMY FLAPJACKS - a 40-year-old hard, hard bastard.

JIMMY THE PRICK - a 30-year-old hard, hard bastard.

> BANGERS
> I'll see your 'monkey' and I'll raise you
> a 'pony'.

[Note for production: they're actually talking about money.]

>FRANKIE THE SNAKE
>I'll see your 'pony' and raise you a
>'score'.

>TOMMY FLAPJACKS
>(Takes a thoughtful munch on some flapjack)
>I'm out.

>BANGERS
>Let's see what you've got.

They turn over their cards. BANGERS has the queen of spades, the queen of hearts, the jack of clubs, the seven of hearts and the three of spades. FRANKIE THE SNAKE has got the king of hearts, the jack of hearts, the nine of hearts, the six of hearts and the two of hearts. JIMMY THE PRICK has got the two of spades, the two of clubs, the three of diamonds, the king of diamonds and the nine of diamonds. TOMMY FLAPJACKS has folded, but out of interest he had the four of diamonds, the five of spades, the nine of clubs, the ten of hearts and the jack of spades. The cards in the flop were as follows: the king of spades, the six of diamonds and the ten of spades.

>BANGERS
>I've got a King High.

>FRANKIE THE SNAKE
>I've got a King Flush.

>JIMMY THE PRICK
>I've got a pair of twos.

>TOMMY FLAPJACKS
>And I folded.

>FRANKIE THE SNAKE
>It looks like I win the money then.

As FRANKIE goes to collect the money, BANGERS sees a card hidden up FRANKIE's sleeve. It's the ten of spades.

>BANGERS
>Frankie the fucking Snake. Why are you
>always cheating at poker?

>FRANKIE THE SNAKE
>Old habits are hard to break.

>BANGERS
>I tell you what isn't hard to break. Your
>face, you nonce!

BANGERS punches FRANKIE THE SNAKE. A fight breaks out and it's fucking insane. It's like the fight in *The Matrix*, only more

amazing. You can't believe what you're seeing. A pearly king
gets thrown through a window. Someone gets stabbed. It's fucking
brilliant.

OLD NELL appears from behind the bar. She's brassy and a bit
mumsy, but everyone respects her, even though she's short. She's
also blonde and in pretty good shape for someone who's in her
mid-70s (she's basically Barbara Windsor). She fires a shotgun in
the air to get their attention. Everyone stops fighting and looks
at OLD NELL.

>                    FRANKIE THE SNAKE
>          Sorry, Old Nell.

Everyone returns to their drinks. Apart from the man who got
stabbed, obviously, as he's dead on the floor. No one even
notices. This kind of thing happens all the time.

>                    OLD NELL
>          I'm glad you came in today actually,
>          Bangers.

>                    BANGERS
>          And why's that, Old Nell?

>                    OLD NELL
>          I've got a job for you.

>                    BANGERS
>          Ain't you heard the news, Old Nell? I'm
>          retired.

>                    OLD NELL
>          I reckon you'll be un-retired when you
>          hear what I've got to tell you.

>                    BANGERS
>          I very much doubt that, Old Nell.

>                    OLD NELL
>          There's something I want you to steal, see.

>                    BANGERS
>          And what's that, Old Nell?

>                    OLD NELL
>          Some bunce.

>                    BANGERS
>          How much bunce?

>                    OLD NELL
>          A lot.

                              BANGERS
          OK, I'm in.

                              OLD NELL
          There's just one condition.

                              BANGERS
          Why doesn't that surprise me, Old Nell?

                              OLD NELL
          I want you to work with Harry.

                              BANGERS
          Are you having a 'tin bath'? I ain't
          working with no one. And certainly not
          this Harry geezer.

                              HARRY (Out of shot)
          I ain't a geezer.

BANGERS turns to see the sexiest woman you've ever seen in your
life. She's got the face of Eva Longoria; the torso (tits) of
Kelly Brook; the legs and arse of Jessica Simpson, and the hair,
lips and teeth of Gisele Bündchen. She drinks pints of Guinness
down in one and likes watching football. She's also a fucking
lying bitch. This is Harry.

                              BANGERS (to OLD NELL)
          Who's this 'sort'?

                              OLD NELL
          Bangers, meet Harry.

                              BANGERS
          Harry's a bird? When you said Harry, I
          just assumed it was a geezer.

                              HARRY
          It's short for Harriet.

                              BANGERS
          I don't care what it's short for, I ain't
          working with you!

                              HARRY (Sexily)
          OK ... but maybe there's something I can
          do to change your mind ...

INTERIOR, BEDROOM - DAY

BANGERS and HARRY are having sex. She's <u>fully nude</u> and we can
see <u>everything</u>. It's **NOT** shot in soft focus; it's shot in very
hard focus and, as I say, we can see <u>everything</u>. (Continued...)

# The Dirty Folder

*(handwritten, struck through: The Story of O)*
*(handwritten, struck through: Through a Class Darkly)*

## A Piece of Literary Erotica in Three Acts
## by Oregon M. Shawcross

## I / Registration

**IT WAS REGISTRATION** day. Registration day, a Thursday, a day like any other. And neither of them could have known that this wasn't going to turn out to be like any other day they'd ever known – how could they? Yet this outcome had been written ~~on the wall~~ in the stars for longer than ~~either of them Cupid God~~ anyone knew.

They were made for one another, ~~Oregon~~ Octavia and Professor ~~Shales Hales Wales~~ Smith. Him, a crusty old monster of a man, Methuselah and Martin Amis ~~and the Beast from Beauty and the Beast~~ all rolled into one; weary, cynical, lost, hankering for firm young flesh. You could tell just from looking at him that his sex life with his wife had dried up months ago, and that they probably weren't even sleeping in the same bedroom any more. And her, the lovely Octavia, with her taut flesh, peachy skin and air of ~~wanton promise well-travelled loucheness~~ ferocious intellectualism. A worldly girl, a sexually experienced girl, but a girl very much in need of a bit more education ~~if you catch my drift~~. It was perfect.

She sat at her desk and gazed upon her quarry. She imagined his enormous throbbing ~~thing member~~ manhood encased in its corduroy prison, and yearned to set it free. She and she alone could see that his cock was a ~~political~~ prisoner ~~like Nelson Mandela~~, yearning for ~~the sexual equivalent of the relaxation of apartheid laws~~ release.

He noticed her.

'Octavia?'

'Yes?'

He asked her a question, something about an essay and whether or not she'd been able to do all the vacation reading. But she knew he was *really* asking, 'Would you like to take me here, now, hard, on the vinyl flooring, never mind who's watching, never mind the 'rules', just do it, you ~~filthy little bitch~~ lovely little thing? Hmm?'

She nodded and handed him her essay, sheets of paper made dirty by her dirty fingers. He took it, adding the dirt of his fingers to the dirt of hers. Their hands touched – their first moment of physical union – and danger danced between them. He was instantly turned on by her tiny waist and extremely broad mind, a combination rarely found in women these days ~~though that's probably not a very feminist thing to say~~. She was attracted to him in the same way that a knight in ~~Sir Gawain the King Arthur books~~ Chaucer a poem might be attracted to a ~~monster ruined castle~~ dragon – he was terra incognita, a mystery to be explored, an old, old thing from yesteryear, a dried-up husk of manhood itching to be made fresh by sipping at the cup filled with the new sweet dew of youth.

She was that cup, and that new sweet dew. She gazed at him, just as she was, both cup and dew, and he turned and held her finger-dirty essay aloft and said:

'This looks fine. Thank you.'

But they both knew what he was really trying to say. The affair had begun.


## II / Paris

**THEY YEARNED TO** go to Paris. Longed for it ~~even more powerfully than that woman in Revolutionary Road who wanted to go to Paris and ended up giving herself an abortion in the bath.~~ But like so many trapped people in so many novels – novels which, ironically, they had both read and enjoyed – it just wasn't logistically possible. So they were forced to create their own Paris, to build their very own Bastille within the confines of room 267 of the Holiday Inn, Debdale Services off the Manchester Orbital. Which in a way was better for them than actually going to Paris – they were both dreamers, both creative, both poets at their core. And ~~Oregon~~ Octavia was happily blessed with an erotic spark powerful enough to light a barbecue city. Her very presence, as she lounged across the bed in her brand-new well-worn silken underwear from ~~Jigsaw~~ Chanel made a boudoir of the dingy room. As she lay sprawled, a wild hot thing of sex, in her mind the polyester sheets turned to silk, the mattress to goose down, and the fag-ash-smelling bleak quotidian curtains became soft, glossy silken drapes ~~which would probably remind you slightly of a vagina if you looked at them in a certain way~~

We need not go into how they got there. Suffice to say they had been ushered into the arms of Eros as generations of lovers had been before them. They'd moved from looks to words to touch, their mutual desire reaching such a peak that running away together seemed the only thing to do, ~~even though they could only run way on Wednesday evening because that was the only night his wife Jean wasn't in.~~

They were the masters of pretence. Professor Smith had told his wife that he was going to Pilates. Octavia had fooled her young, simple, comparatively sexually inexperienced housemates into thinking she was going to an extra class, by taking a folder out with her entitled 'Extra English Class Work', a subterfuge worthy of ~~the wolf in Little Red Riding Hood~~ Shakespeare. That folder sat now on the bedside table, innocent, quivering atop the room service menu, as the naked Professor Smith reared up over the end of the bed, his ~~manhood member~~ throbbing ~~equipment~~ dick rising sharply upwards like ~~a ski jump Tower Bridge~~ a terrifying sword. It was like a Woody Allen film meets Belle de Jour meets that bit in American Beauty where she lies on her back in the rose petals ~~like a starfish wearing loads of red lipstick.~~

Professor Smith shuffled forwards until he was atop Octavia, hovering over her. Their eyes met, momentarily. She was struck once again by his great, great age, his body ravaged by the years, hair sprouting frond-like from his gaping nostrils, his abdominal wall beginning to collapse outward, a wobbling jelloid ball of memories and history and proud excess ~~and beer~~. The things his eyes must have seen, his old, old eyes. The history, the loss, the might of time. It was as if she were being made love to by the past itself, a feeling reinforced by his aftershave, ~~which was something like Old Spice, which had clearly been in the back of the cupboard for quite a long time.~~

He gazed admiringly upon her alabaster body. God, perfection, perfection! From the crown of her ~~coiffured~~ artfully tousled head down to her navel, which seemed, to him, to be some kind of bottomless pool, a ~~messy~~ pond eager to cast forth its secrets. He could wait no longer. He moved down into the area about seven inches below her navel, her ~~private sexual magical naughty~~ exquisite area, and thrust and thrust and thrust, and they were one like Romeo and Juliet, and Troilus and Criseyde, and Anthony and Cleopatra ~~and loads of others~~. He thrust more, thrust longer, thrust so hard that the bed was unable to contain them and they tumbled to the floor. Suddenly, he felt protective of her, of her Lolita-like youth, and he saw fit to pause and whisper, 'Mind you don't bang your back on the radiator.' Which was quite a poignant thing for him to have said, as it reminded Octavia that this situation was at once fiercely erotic and horribly bleak. And as he took her from behind she gazed out through the window into the car park, where she saw two ugly dogs fucking against a wheelie bin. She saw the dogs, and ~~like that man in the Proust book looking at the biscu~~it she mourned childhood losses, and suddenly wondered if she was doing this because of some unresolved psychological issues with her father, who'd always expressed his love for her in terms of money, ~~buying her a horse when he could have just said sorry for missing the school play~~. She swiftly put those thoughts out of her mind as Professor Smith climaxed inside her, making a noise like a waste disposal unit.

## III / The end of the affair

**THE TITLE OF** this act is deliberately misleading, as the affair continues to this day. Stolen moments, the Holiday Inn, the radiator, the carpet, ~~the trouser press,~~ the fraudulent folder wobbling atop the room service menu on the bedside table. Professor Smith's towering ~~sword sceptre meat prick member~~ shaft ~~hopping darting~~ plunging into her area Wednesday after Wednesday, a top-secret guest, like an MI5 agent at an embassy ball in the 1950s.

And who knows where it will go, where this story will end? It would be easy to predict disaster, as Octavia's housemate ~~Ved~~ Susannah seems only too keen to do, ~~judgemental bitch~~ wailing Cassandra that she is. And it would be easy to predict a happy ending as well, perhaps like that of a Shakespearean comedy ~~like The Comedy of Errors or As You~~ Like It ~~or Much Ado About Nothing~~. But the easiest route is not always the most interesting in literary terms, so maybe it would be best to leave this one open. Nobody knows what will happen next. It is unknowable. The only thing that we can know for certain is that Octavia is one of the bravest and most beautiful young women in the whole of the Greater Manchester area, and always will be. No matter what anyone else might say to her, or behind her back, she has been braver than any of them would ever be.

She's like a cross between Helen of Troy and a social worker, really, providing sexual respite care for a man in a woefully unhappy marriage. So if you're going to get all arsey and 'meh meh meh, you shouldn't be shagging a married dude' about this, then I suggest you just keep your big nose out of it.

Anyway. It is a far, far better thing that I do than I have ever done. The rest is silence.


O. M. Shawcross (2012)

# Break Free:
# (Break Free the Sha[ck]les!)

A collection of poetry
by Oregon M. Shawcross

## Introduction

O. M. Shawcross is a modern poet with a bold and unconventional approach to both subject matter and formatting. In her debut publication 'Break Free: (Break Free the Sha[ck]les!)' she brings us, for the first time, her unique style. She is the natural descendant – one might even say the imaginary love child – of Emily Dickinson and Bob Dylan. Lyrical, raw and with a searing honesty that will cut you to the quick, her poetry also reflects the spirit of our times.

In pieces such as 'We Marched for Justice and We Got Nothing', she screams of the disillusionment facing today's young people. While in other pieces, such as 'Humbert My Humbert', we see her ponder a more personal subject matter: her infamous relationship with university lecturer Tony Shales, an eminent academic of his time. Their tempestuous relationship was typical of that which happens between artists, depending little on the approval of society, and operating under its own chaotic, passion-driven rules. Ultimately, however, Shawcross was too free a spirit to be tied down for long, and the breakdown of their love affair, and the inevitable pain it caused Shales, is acutely represented on these pages in poems such as 'His Hands Look Older Than They Did Before'.

This is not poetry for the faint-hearted, or for the grammar snob. Shawcross is a trailblazer when it comes to punctuation, just one of the elements of her work that sets her apart as a revolutionary artist of her time.

# Table of Contents

fresheR                                                page 110

Humbert My Humbert                                     page 111

Is a Father Like a Horse?                              page 111

MRS                                                    page 112

We Marched for Justice and We Got Nothing              page 112

His Hands Look Older Than They Did Before              page 113

About the Author                                       page 113

## fresheR

open to new experience: strive to survive wide-Eyed (but not nAïve) that's mE i
am: arriveD

here

in manchesteR

maDchesteR

good times

are on their way

today

tomorroW

the next day

and for 3 years after that till

graduatioN

literally the grade-atioN of my existencE resistancE to that idea is naturaL for a rebeL
such as mE. freE. I aM, facT. Unfettered to be exacT. unshackleD by social constraintS
the restraints others live bY drive by (in their carS) vehicles of despaiR monuments to
'societY' BEWARE (because I've got an:)

infatuatioN

with rebellioN to change the worlD i aiM. insanE? perhapS. but the line is finE
between mad-nesS and geni-uS so they say and who am I? 2 arguE. that's my drivE. 2
argue makes me feel . . . alivE.

## Humbert My Humbert

I see you across the seminar room your eyes meet mine and electricity passes
between us in that one glance askance (Humbert) we gaze as if we might erase
time's discrepancy its cruel obsession with passage/forwards motion/
sans emotion/sans care or as they say (Humbert): 'senza la donna no more pain no
more
sorrow' what does that mean?
*who knows!* It just *goes to show* how little **anything** can be said to mean **anything**
in matters of the <3 [heart] when love is real, Humbert we start – not to 'in-tell-ect-ual-
ize' but instead to feel. Humbert Humbert my Humbert how I long for you . . .
Humbert, do you feel as I? If so please Humbert give me a sign.

## Is a Father Like a Horse?

No, they said: A horse is not like a father, they said. A horse is less than a parent,
they said.
Can a horse they said be loved
    as a person? Can the loss of a horse they said, be worse than a man?
And I said:
yes
it can.

## MRS or 'What it feels like to be the other woman'

Dark secrets lie with me a'night comfort me, hold me in their hot-FIngeREd
embrace a trace of heady guilt the lingering scent of his body, his Kisses serves to
reMind me of you: Mrs.
COld remnants stay with him a'while his memOries Of yOur steely wOrds, yOur
icy face the chrOme-plated place yOu share where/yOu work/he dOes the dishes:
hOw alOne he is with yOu: O cOld Mrs.
They call you Mrs
but tis I who am his true life wife – notyou!ButI – :
hot Young wife of his Heart
nOt Old COld wife Of the Past.

## We Marched for Justice and We Got Nothing

We marched for justice and we got surrounded hounded astounded by unfounded
accusations of political unrest.
We marched for justice and we got kettled tested on our mettle expected to settle
(in a way which nettled) for second best.
We marched for justice and we got arrested suspected not respected our attempt to
protest unmolested taught us: youth of today you have no rights left!
We marched for justice then we got the coach back pitch black drove on the inside
track to hit the sack and dream our longed-for future.

# His Hands Look Older Than They Did Before

My alabaster skin gleams in the gloaming Candles he has lit, his eye – once roaming – Now has itself (ie eyes) for me only.

His hands look older than I thought them When deep in love it was that first I sought them Now suddenly (it seems) I'm not so sure.

Fickle! Thy name is Oregon! Oh heart: –

Can you change your mind without a warning? Must we don the blacks and start our mourning?? For this once great love, is the end dawning???

In the candlelight, my heart begins to break – – Not for itself, for him! My eyes (once clear with love for him) become opaque A creature such as I cannot remain enslaved:

Escape!! ! !!!                     !!

!

!!! !                   !    !!!  !!          !

Break break! Fling open the cage door!

Oregon M. Shawcross was born in Surrey and is currently a student at Manchester University. She has travelled around the globe and lists her inspirations as: Gandhi, Emily Dickinson, Bob Dylan, the wisdom of little children, the Dalai Lama, Janis Joplin, the Qu'ran and the way the sun sets over the ocean in Thailand.

With thanks to: Violet Nordstrom, Professor Tony Shales, Professor Jean Shales, Mr and Mrs N. Shawcross, the English Department and Manchester University

For Roulette. Always Loved. Never Forgotten.

# Helpless

**By Tony Shales**

www.abctales.com/story/tonyshales/helpless

**HE WASN'T AT** all what she had expected. Surely, she thought upon entering the classroom, this man isn't the notorious 40-something-year-old author and professor Thomas Clay? He can't possibly be old enough. But it was he. She found herself transfixed. Despite his surprisingly youthful appearance, that acclaimed charisma could hardly belong to anyone else.

Clay stood astride a chair at the front of the class, and her eyes wandered towards his manly thighs, clasping the wooden frame betwixt them like two great columns. Try not to think about his other column! The thought was in her mind before she could stop it, and Alabama Crossley blushed fiercely, pushing a strand of thick glossy brown hair behind her ear. She took a seat at the back of the class. All the better to spy on you, Tommy, she thought to herself, opening his groundbreaking text and marvelling once again at the insights contained therein.

Reading his tome had not only changed her mind, it had changed her life. She owed him a debt she thought it unlikely she could ever repay. Although, as she sat there, admiring his pert buttocks, his wide chest, his finely chiselled jaw and the shock of thick dark hair which few men of his age could boast the like of, she found herself thinking of all sorts of ways Tommy Clay might possibly be repaid . . .

**HE WAS A** man of honour. It had been said of him that, although his middle name was Simon, it should by rights have been Integrity. The student–teacher relationship was something he had always considered sacred. Not to mention the bond of marriage, however difficult it had been – married all these years to a woman so clearly his intellectual inferior that sometimes he struggled to make Jennifer understand even the simplest of instructions. Tommy Clay stared at his own handsome face in the mirror. Of course he didn't think of himself as handsome, his mind was on higher things. Nevertheless, despite his unawareness, he was extraordinarily attractive. Students had always been attracted to him, yes. This one wasn't the first. But he couldn't deny it, the way she had looked at him when she spoke about his book – it had reached inside him to a place . . . a place which had remained untouched for too many years. Too many years of stilted, lowbrow conversation around the dinner table with Jennifer.

At last, Tommy felt, here was a woman who had glimpsed into the infinite reaches of his mind. Dammit, Tommy. She's not a woman. She's a girl! A girl, dammit! He grasped the edges of the porcelain sink, until his knuckles turned as white as the porcelain sink. But at the same time, god – it was obvious that however young she was, the girl was no innocent. That was obvious from the way she walked. The clothes she wore. Tommy's good-looking features were ravaged with guilt as the dilemma passed across them: the girl was coming over to clean his microwave. And she would be here any moment . . .

**ALABAMA'S HEART POUNDED** with anticipation. Waiting there at the front door, she knew this was by far the biggest thing that would ever happen to her in her life. To be invited to his house. The honour of wiping the dirt from his microwave. Shivering a little with nerves, she glanced up at the impressive mansion he lived in, realizing that it was only a matter of time before one of the famous blue plaques would adorn his wall. For a brief second, she wondered how it would feel to be Tommy's wife – knowing that the aforementioned plaque would bear his name and his name alone, despite the fact that she too was a professor in the same field. No one could doubt however that Tommy was the genius. Tommy was the one whose works would be remembered throughout history. Tommy was . . . opening the door!

Alabama blushed fiercely, tucking a loose strand of hair behind her ear. She adjusted her blouse, tugging it down to reveal more of her pert young breasts. She smoothed her palms over the sluttishly short skirt, deliberately chosen to entice, to seduce, to render Tommy helpless to her charms. Alabama knew exactly what to do with men. And no matter how extraordinarily clever Tommy was, despite the fact that he was one of the great thinkers of his time, she could tell that he was also a hot-blooded male. He was a man with a powerful sexuality. That kind of charisma just couldn't be denied. She fluttered her eyelashes, gazing up at the man himself standing dominantly in the doorway. His eyes raked over her body with undisguised lust – but just in time he remembered himself – beckoning her into the living room and closing the door behind him. Sitting on the sofa, her shapely legs uncrossed, Alabama was aware that Tommy was a man of high morals, a devoted husband and family man. But everyone also knew that his wife was a bimbo who didn't understand him.

And anyway, Alabama didn't care about trivial things like morals. She was going to get her claws into Tommy. And once she did – there was no way she was letting go. He was going to be powerless, once she had turned on her witchy charms. There would be literally nothing he could do to stop it . . .

**NOT MANY MEN** have the capacity to feel guilt while simultaneously thrusting their generously proportioned manhood into a hot young vessel. As he pleasured her, Tommy could tell that Alabama had never had a lover like him before. She gasped, her glistening eyes wet with tears and astonishment, as he brought her to her joyous peak over and over again, only allowing himself the momentary release once he was sure she could take no more.

And as they lay there, their bodies entwined – hers young and beautiful, his a little bit older but still strong and firm as a man of half his age – Tommy reflected that sometimes extraordinary people are allowed to transgress the laws of everyday life. Could he help being a great artist? Of course not. He stroked his fingers over Alabama's pert young breasts, tantalizing her once more, remembering a quotation from another great man, Fyodor Dostoevsky, about how extraordinary people are allowed to transgress the laws of everyday life. Alabama rolled on top of him and begged him to penetrate her once again. And naturally, because he was extraordinary in so very many ways, Tommy was already ready to go again . . .

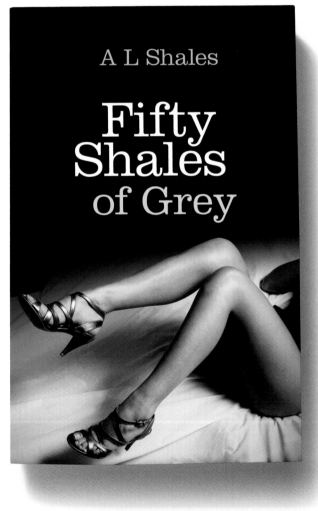

A L Shales

# Fifty Shales of Grey

## Charity Blind Date Form

Please return your completed form to your charity blind date rep by 6 February or else you won't get a date in time for Valentine's Day!

**Name:** Oregon

**Subject:** English

**I'm looking for:** I'm not looking for anything. Stuff like student dating is always sort of bullshit, isn't it? I don't really give a shit if you're handsome, or if you like travelling, or if you think that maybe, maybe, really, there isn't anything wrong with fox hunting as long as you do it humanely. But yeah, I don't really care about any of that.

**Me in five words:** Too complex for five words

**Idea of a perfect date:**

I'm sure lots of girls put down all the usual fairytale tripe: a candlelit dinner, Prince Charming riding up on a horse made of commitment, stuff like that. But I'd prefer something more real - maybe we'd go for a drink and talk about blood diamonds or what happens after we die, just cut through all the fake bollocks and make a proper connection.

**Worst date ever:**

When I was 17 a guy I liked asked me to watch his band, Cause for Concern, play a gig. I stood right at the front so he would know I'd made it to the show, but it turned out he already had a girlfriend and I had tinnitus for ten days afterwards.

**Unusual talent:**

I played Judas in our Year 10 production of Jesus Christ, Superstar.

**Karaoke favourite:**

'Babooshka' by Kate Bush. Not an obvious karaoke choice, but I'm not an obvious girl.

**You will recognize me because:**

If it's meant to happen, it'll happen

# Sext Messages by Shales

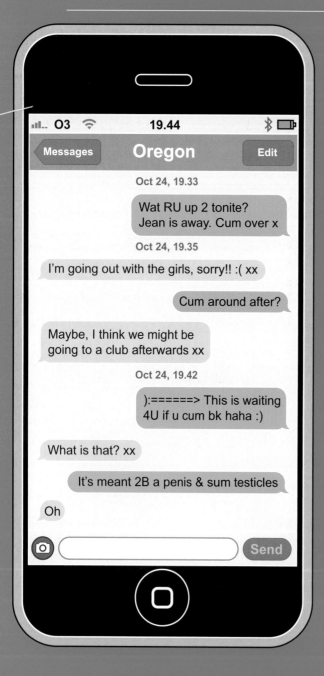

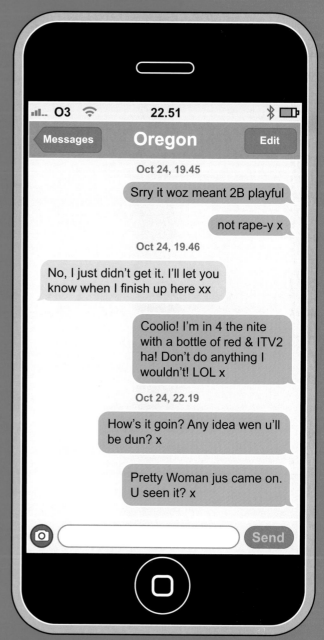

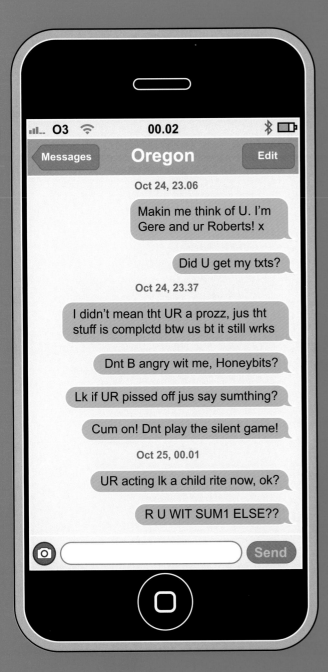

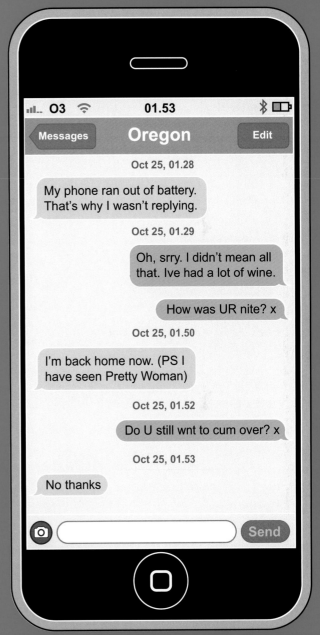

# Mind the Gap

by Oregon Shawcross

The difficult thing about having had a 'gap year' is how much more mature you are than 99% of the freshers you meet when you arrive at university. Once you've supped Lapsang Souchong on the slopes of the Himalayas with monks who've had personal conversations with the Dalai Lama[1], you might find it hard to talk about *The X Factor* or other aspects of superficial, meaningless life in Britain.

Once you've ridden an elephant through the jungles of Goa[2], or smoked the finest opium in the poppy fields of Afghanistan[3], or trekked through the Andes with no one but a donkey as your guide[4], then really, what challenge is there on the outskirts of Manchester with a bunch of spotty youths, most of whom have never ventured further than northern France? Some, believe it or not, have never been abroad. The sheer ignorance of people who've never bothered to travel won't cease to amaze you. How anyone can choose to abstain from the fabulous reaches of our beautiful world – all of which are a mere plane ride away – is beyond me.

And not just because of the wonderful volcanoes and waterfalls either. Don't get me wrong, I want to take in the whole spectrum of what this world has to offer. I've seen beggars on the streets of Mumbai, and street kids in Rio – on the streets[5] – while some people here in the UK, where we are all so rich, seem to have no desire to witness these horrors first hand. Talk about heads in the sand!

Having said that, if people choose not to travel because of the environmental impact of flying, then that's different. But please note that coaches and trains are available, as well as cruise ships. I'm all in favour of a lengthy bus journey, where one can meet all types of old local peasant women and experience the true nature of a country, e.g., Indonesia.

1. I have literally done this – one of the monks hadn't just spoken to the Dalai Lama but actually went to school with his cousin.
2. I really want to do this.
3. Hashtag wishlist!
4. I met an awesome guy in Caracas who had actually done this.
5. Mind-blowing documentary we watched in sixth form – totally made me want to go to Rio.

## Compassion

The reason I'm writing this is to help those of you who may have had a gap year to adjust to life among those I like to call 'home-leavers'. It would be all too easy to dismiss these innocents as ignorant people who don't know their Mancala stones from their Carrom board but, as Buddha himself would probably say if he was at uni, freshers deserve compassion.

Rather than judge them for their ignorant attitudes and lack of life experience, instead let us pity them for their narrow-minded approach to life. If I hear that someone has only ever been to, say, Spain (on some gross 18–30s holiday) then instead of belittling their so-called adventure (where they probably ate bacon and eggs and drank beer in the 'Queen Vic'), I try to educate them about the advantages of setting off along the road less-travelled, with little more than a *Rough Guide* in your hand and an open-spirited approach to the friendly natives.

## Perspective

We have a lot to teach the home-leavers, and the most important lesson we have for them is that of perspective. The kind of global vision you gain from a gap year is something most people who come from, for example, Northampton will just have no idea about – yet. But that doesn't mean we can't enlighten them. Facebook albums, souvenirs, amusing anecdotes about the time you spent in a Buddhist monastery, all of these things can open the minds of your fellow students and help them realize that their own minor troubles aren't so important after all. It can be really useful for people who are complaining about, for example, 'Boo hoo my student loan hasn't come through,' or whatever, to be reminded that there are places in the world that not only don't have student loans, they don't even have universities. In some parts of Africa they don't even have their own football teams, and are forced to support our English premier league.

For me, it's really important to take the lessons learned on my gap year and teach them to those around us. Our wisdom ranges from the small and domestic – herbal tea does not require milk, authentic Indian people do not eat chicken tikka masala – to bigger and more important information such as, orphans are REAL and still alive today.

Not only was the gap year of benefit to us personally, it can now be used for the good of all, which is a truly important 'global' perspective.

Thanks for taking the time to read. Om Shanti.

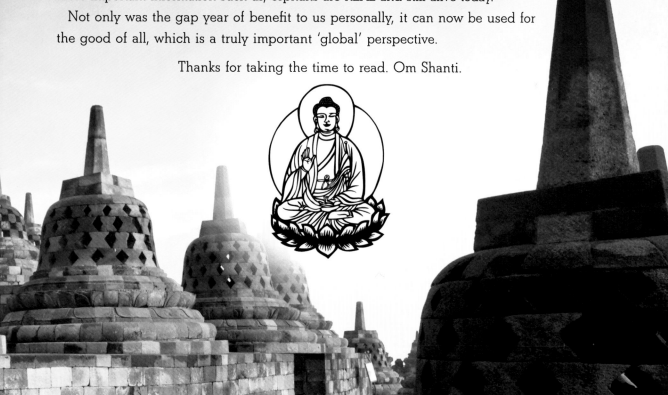

# Kingsley's Guide to University Societies

Starting uni can be a really stressful time for most people and there's a lot to worry about – making new friends, trying to figure out how long you can go without washing your clothes and, the absolute worst part, the Freshers' Fair.

There's no real way to describe the horrors of Freshers' Fair in full, but it's kind of like if you've ever been abroad, got slightly lost and then ended up in a weird street market. Except, instead of bootleg copies of *Mission Impossible 4* and tables covered in exotic, but essentially inedible, meats, there are just loads of stalls with overenthusiastic twats wearing matching T-shirts, clutching a bunch of free pens. Everyone there is trying to get you to sign up to their club. They'll all claim to be really cool and try to give you fun badges and stuff, but don't be sucked in! They're just taking advantage of the fact that you're a little lonely and probably haven't eaten anything except Pringles and dry cereal since your parents dropped you off a few days ago.

I signed up to the Gilbert and Sullivan society just to get the guy holding the clipboard to stop singing stuff from *The Pirates of Penzance* directly at me. I ended up being dragged to about three rehearsals before I figured out how to unsubscribe from their mailing list.

The worst bit is that some of the societies will even make you pay sign-up fees, and thanks to a mixture of excitement, naivety and an astonishingly humid sports hall, lots of people end up forking over a fair slice of their student loan, and all they get in return is a mouse pad or something.

The real trick to navigating your way round the Freshers' Fair is to know which societies and groups to go for and which ones to avoid. I've put together a brief rundown of some of the trickier people you'll come across, so that hopefully you won't make the same mistakes that I made ...

## Hare Krishna Society

Definitely give these guys your e-mail address. They put you on a mailing list and then give out free lunches twice a week. The food almost always looks like a bowl of 'yellow', but it's surprisingly good! To be honest, I don't know why the other religious groups don't try doing a similar thing, because loads of people always turn up. I'm sure Jehovah's Witnesses would have way more luck if they went around with a Sunday roast or something.

## Young Conservative Society

Not surprisingly, these guys aren't very popular with students, what with the education cuts and shutting down libraries and making orphans wrestle (or whatever sick stuff conservatives do in private). But watch out, because they try and persuade freshers to sign up by putting the fittest people in the society behind the desk. There's one insanely beautiful girl who's there every year – apparently she's 28, but they keep paying for her to do post-grad courses, just so that she can come back to help recruit people.

## Ultimate Frisbee Society

On the surface this looks like a really fun, chilled-out way to make friends and get some exercise, but don't be fooled! Ultimate Frisbee guys are super-intense about what they do. I think it's because they're compensating for the fact that throwing around a frisbee is one of the most frivolous things you can do with your time. Seriously, any 'sport' where you could replace one of the players with a dog probably doesn't deserve uniforms and a scoring system.

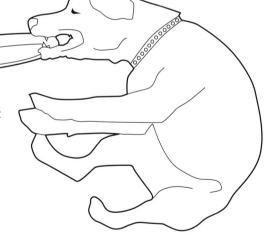

## Anarchist Society

Ironically, these guys always have one of the most organized stalls at the fair. Last year they had a guy giving free ear-piercings at their desk, but this was stopped after a bunch of people got really bad infections and a few of them developed blood poisoning. I guess things like risk assessments and sterilization aren't very nihilistic, but they are sort of there for a reason.

## Friends of Palestine Society

For some reason this stall is directly next to the Support Israel Society. It does seem like poor planning and things always get kind of tense around that bit of the sports hall. My advice would be to do what I did and sign up for both of them.

## 'Sexpertise' Society

These guys are like the sexual health branch of the Student Union and they're always trying to recruit new members. They make it sound like a really cool way to meet people, but almost everyone involved in the society is either über-Christian or a borderline nympho. Plus, they call themselves 'sexperts', but I don't really think standing outside a nightclub at two o'clock on a Wednesday morning, handing out condoms and free lube, makes you an expert in anything.

Like I said, the Freshers' Fair really is a minefield, but I thought I'd finish off with probably my most important bit of advice – sooner or later you'll realize that a lot of the societies and groups you come across don't actually do anything and they're basically just an excuse for nerds to meet up and eventually have sex with one another.

Below is a list of all the societies that are essentially just geeky swingers' clubs:

- Junior Aerospace Society
- Renaissance Society
- Tea Society
- Céilidh Society
- Model UN
- Amnesty International
- Real Ale Society
- Jazz Society
- Student LibDem Society

- Medieval Society
- Medieval and Renaissance Society
- Engineers without Borders
- A Cappella Society (aka The Four Tune Tellers)
- Quiz Society
- The Canoeing Club
- Trampoline Society
- Circus Skills Society
- Computer Programming Club

## Charity Blind Date Form

Please return your completed form to your charity blind date rep by 6 February or else you won't get a date in time for Valentine's Day!

**Name:** Kingsley

**Subject:** Geology. I did a bit of Drama too, but now I'm back on Geology. It's kind of a long story, to do with a girl. Well, two girls really. It's actually quite romantic, in a sort of annoying 'I really wish most of that hadn't happened' kind of way.

**I'm looking for:** Just a fun night with a fun girl! (Not in a creepy way or anything.)

**Me in five words:** fun, good listener, non-threatening.

**Idea of a perfect date:**

We would do something romantic, but not pretentious, maybe dinner at d Jamie's Italian and then bowling?

**Worst date ever:**

I surprised a girl with tickets to go on the London Eye, but it turned out she had vertigo. She threw up three times and we were stuck in the pod for another 15 minutes.

**Unusual talent:** I'm pretty much the Yo-Yo Ma of yo-yoing. Just kidding, but I do really know how to yo-yo.

**Karaoke favourite:** 'All Along The Watchtower' – preferably the Dylan version, but I'd do the Hendrix one if that was all they had.

**You will recognize me because:**

I will be carrying a red rose and a yo-yo.

# Dan the lecturer's friend requests to Kingsley

25/9/11

**New Message**

To: Kingsley ✕

Subject: Buds! YAY!

Message: Hey, Kingsley! I noticed you nodding off in this morning's lecture and I'm majorly pissed off! Just kidding, it's honestly fine. Trust me, I've been there, too – after a night out sweating your tits off to acid-rave the last thing you want is to listen to someone bang on about layered mafic intrusions and Hawaiian basalts (!) Anyway, just sending out my legendary start-of-term friend requests. Rock on!

Dan the Geology Man

Send   Cancel

25/10/11

**New Message**

To: Kingsley ✕

Subject: Hey, dude!

Message: Hey K-Man! I tried sending you a friend request at the start of term, but I don't think it went through properly (Zuckerburg, you bloody bastard!), so I thought I'd send through another one.

Dan the Geology Man

Send   Cancel

**New Message**

To: Kingsley ✕

Subject: You've got to check this out, man!

Message:

Kingsley in da house! I wanted to post this great video on your wall, but I realized that we weren't actually Facebook friends yet . . . crazy?!
Anyway, take a look at the link below. It's by these cool geologists from America who change the lyrics of famous rock songs so that they're actually about rocks! 'Walk the Alkaline', 'Bridge Over Thermodynamic Magmatic Systems' – fun stuff like that.

http://www.youtube.com/watch?v=bsdPOerdffr

If you like that stuff, you can always send me your email address and I'll cc you into a great email chain I've got going with a couple of other guys in the faculty?

Dan

Send  Cancel

**New Message**

To: Kingsley ✕

Subject: Hi!

Message:

Hi, Kingsley! Did you ever get a chance to check out that video? :-)

D x

Send  Cancel

## New Message

| | |
|---|---|
| **To:** | Kingsley ✕ |
| **Subject:** | I get it |
| **Message:** | Hello, Kingsley. I guess you don't want to be my Facebook friend – especially seeing as you have ignored FOUR previous friend requests … |
| | I know you think you're really 'cool' right now, but let me tell you, time will catch up with you! One day you're a young hotshot skipping a lecture to go and watch *Groundhog Day* with your girlfriend, the next thing you know it's 10 years later and you're up at 1a.m. ordering pills from the internet that reverse male pattern baldness. |
| | Anyway, ignore me, I'm just overreacting I guess. It's not a big deal and it's *probably* not the sort of thing I'll remember when it comes to marking end-of-module exams or writing references for future internships. |
| | Dan |

**Send**  Cancel

## New Message

| | |
|---|---|
| **To:** | Kingsley ✕ |
| **Subject:** | I'm sorry |
| **Message:** | Hello again. |
| | A quick follow-up re my last friend request. I just want to clarify in writing that I was not suggesting – nor would I ever suggest – that I would allow something as trivial as a series of rejected friend requests to influence my treatment of any student (even if he or she has treated me like a bit of a dick). |
| | In conclusion, I apologize and there's no need for this to go any further than between the two of us (including the hair stuff). |
| | Thank you, Dan |

**Send**  Cancel

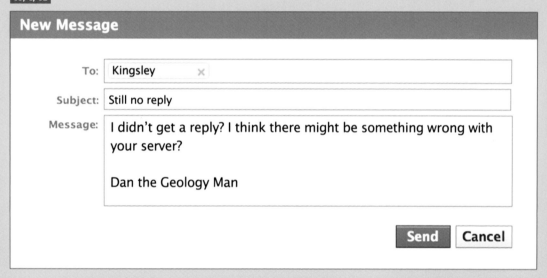

13/3/12

**New Message**

To: Kingsley ✕

Subject: Hello!

Message: Special K! Thought I'd try my luck with the friend request one more time (!) Catch you later!

Dan the Geology Man

**Send**   Cancel

13/4/12

**New Message**

To: Kingsley ✕

Subject: Still no reply

Message: I didn't get a reply? I think there might be something wrong with your server?

Dan the Geology Man

**Send**   Cancel

## Charity Blind Date Form

Please return your completed form to your charity blind date rep by 6 February or else you won't get a date in time for Valentine's Day!

**Name:** Josie

**Subject:** Dentistry

**I'm looking for:** Nothing serious, just a nice evening and hopefully a new friend! But if anything else happens then great! You never know what kind of connection you might make with a stranger. For all I know you could be a psycho who tricks nice girls into dates, kills them, empties out their bodies and then uses them as some sort of sick human bookcase! I'm sure you don't do that.

**Me in five words:** Easy-going, bubbly girl. Nothing's more important to me than friends and family, because they're always there for you. Sorry, that's way more than five words...

**Idea of a perfect date:** Drinking champagne in a hot air balloon while Ryan Gosling (who's wearing a tux) serenades me on the piano. I don't know exactly how you get a piano into a hot air balloon, but if anyone can figure it out, it's Ryan Gosling ☺

**Worst date ever:** On our 18-month anniversary my ex-boyfriend Dave took me to watch his cousin Lloyd play rugby in the SWALEC cup quarter-finals against Llandovery. His cousin got a concussion at the start of the second half and we spent the rest of the day in A&E.

**Unusual talent:**

**Karaoke favourite:**

**You will recognize me because:**

mᴙoᖷ ɘƚɒᗡ bnila ⊽ƚiᴙɒʜϽ

Pleɒꙅɘ ᴙɘƚuᴙn ⊽ouᴙ ɔomϱleƚɘb moᖷ oƚ ⊽ouᴙ ɔʜɒᴙiƚ⊽ blinb
ɘƚɒb ᴙɘϱ ⊽b 8 ⊽ᴙɒuᴙdɘᖷ oᴙ ɘꙅlɘ ⊽ou won'ƚ ᵷɘƚ ɒ ɘƚɒb ni ɘmiƚ
ᴙoᖷ Vɒlɘnƚinɘ'ꙅ ⊽ɒᗡ!

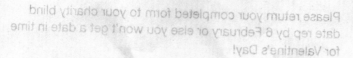

**Unusual talent:**

*I can give you a free dental exam!*

**Karaoke favourite:**

*'Faith' by George Michael.*

**You will recognize me because:**

*I'll be carrying a copy of the Girl with the Dragon Tattoo (great book btw!) x*

## Charity Blind Date Form

Please return your completed form to your charity blind date rep by 6 February or else you won't get a date in time for Valentine's Day!

**Name:** HOWARD

**Subject:** GEOLOGY, For now

**I'm looking for:** Nothing.

**Me in five words:** No

**Idea of a perfect date:** My house. There is nothing you could want to do on a diet that wouldn't be available (and more convenient). Food, music, movies and contraception are all readily available through the internet. I'd also be by myself.

**Worst date ever:** N/A, but once we had a package at the house that was delivered by a woman, I told her that I'd never seen a woman postman before and she said that there were actually quite a few of them, although they are less common than men.

**Unusual talent:** I can always tell when somebody is about to sneeze.

**Karaoke favourite:** I've never done karaoke and I almost certainly never will. Even in some alternate dystopian future, where people wear matching jump suits and the government force people to sing pop songs, I think I'd still refuse and take the mandatory hard labour.

**You will recognize me because:** I will have a copy of my birth certificate.

## Charity Blind Date Form

Please return your completed form to your charity blind date rep by 6 February or else you won't get a date in time for Valentine's Day!

**Name:** VOD

**Subject:** Booze, pills, English and general shit.

**I'm looking for:**

**Me in five words:** I'm a fucking English Rose.

**Idea of a perfect date:** It's a friday night, and we kick the whole thing off with my homemade cocktail, the Tropical Hurricane — it's Malibu, Sainsbury's basics whisky and green vodka sourz. We go to the pub, plant ourselves at the bar and get properly fucked, until last orders. Then we find somewhere that's playing music. If it's shitty music we can bung a load of drugs — weed, coke, modafinil, prescription cough medicine, whatever's going basically. After that we split a lamb doner on the way home, then take two Xanax to bring on the comedown and watch late night poker on TV.

**Worst date ever:** For bullshit legal reasons i'm not allowed to talk about my worst date. But without going into specifics, let's just say that I was fucked out of 150 qrid and a trip on the Eurostar.

**Unusual talent:** I've never broken a bone in my body. Been X-rayed on eight seperate occasions, but not one single fracture. I'm indestructible!

**Karaoke favourite:** 'Welcome to the Jungle' by Guns N' Roses.

**You will recognize me because:** I'll get in touch with you. Trust me, it's safer for you that way.

# JP's Eulogy to his Dad

I wrote this eulogy for my dad's funeral, but at the last minute the vicar told me I wasn't allowed to read it out – something about the service running late and not being allowed to say the word 'fucktank' on Church of England property. Anyway, I thought I'd stick it in here so that I can at least get the words out somewhere – hopefully he's up in heaven, reading this and having a whiskey while Mother Teresa gives him a hand job or something . . .

The Oxford English Dictionary defines a funeral as 'a ceremony or service held shortly after a person's death, usually including the person's burial or cremation', and d'you know what [pause for dramatic effect] they're right. But there's one word the Oxford English Dictionary can't define [longer pause for more dramatic effect] sadness.

My dad wasn't just the man who put a baby inside my mum, he was like a father, older brother, fun cousin and uncle who lets you drink at his house all wrapped up in a Savile Row suit.

Yes, sometimes he could be a little bit distant – he never visited me at boarding school or signed my birthday cards in person – but I know that he loved me and he gave me so much. And I'm not just talking about money, although he did often give me a lot of money if I promised to be quiet for a while.

He was the man who paid a nanny to teach me how to ride a bike. He was the man who taught me never to give money to homeless people because they'll just spend it on cider and smack. And most importantly he was the man who taught me how to be a man.

A lot of the time funerals can be seriously fucking bum-out events, but that's not what Dad would have wanted, so I want everyone here to appreciate the good times they had with him.

I remember when I was 14 and he took me to Lord's to watch an Ashes Test match. We were sharing a hospitality box with a couple of Aussie bastards, and between every over he'd whisper funny stuff to make me laugh like, 'I hope we trounce these aborigine-killing, ex-convict, wallaby fucktanks' – that's just the kind of great guy he was.

So, Dad, I'd just like to finish by saying that I'm really, really, really going to miss you. Like Biggie and Tupac, you were taken from us way too fucking early, and though you weren't necessarily gunned down because of gang affiliation, it's a reminder for all of us to keep our eyes open for the silent drive-by shooting that is heart disease. Dad, I'm pouring one out for you now – fuck things up in the afterlife.

## Charity Blind Date Form

Please return your completed form to your charity blind date rep by 6 February or else you won't get a date in time for Valentine's Day!

**Name:** JP Everyone calls me JP, but you can call me 'The Bucking Fucking Bronco'.

**Subject:** Advanced Pussy Studies.

**I'm looking for:** One night of no-strings-attached bedroom action. It doesn't have to be a bedroom though, I'm very happy mixing up the locale

**Me in five words:** Great banter and sexually gifted.

**Idea of a perfect date:**

Two models (one blonde, one brunette) in a hotel room, unlimited room service and a buffet breakfast in the morning.

**Worst date ever:**

When my mate Chizz turned 21, me and a few pals went on a lads' weekend trip to Zagreb. Lagers cost like 80p, so we all got smashed and chatted up a group of Croatian girls. I brought the hottest one back to the hostel, but when I tried ~~taking~~ things to the next level she got fucking weird, pulled out a small blade and stole my passport. I had to go to the British embassy to get a new one the next morning.

**Unusual talent:**

On the first day of sixth form there was an initiation ritual where the upper VI made us drink three shots of vodka through a fish — I was the only person who didn't throw up.

**Karaoke favourite:**

'Party and Bullshit' by The Notorious B.I.G. The words 'party' and 'bullshit' basically sum up my teenage years, and my years now as well really.

**You will recognize me because:**

I'll be the dude fighting off other chicks in the corner.

# Blaster
## Freshers' Supplement
gig guide, nights out and much more

# Academy Showcase Review

A storm is brewing. A new tide is rising. And it seeks to clash itself in all its youthful beauty over the pathetic ramparts of a culture grown fat and bloated, eating its own stupidity.

Who could not have had such thoughts while 'watching' the recent showcase at the Academy. A line-up which, in its very typeface, reeked of an old order begging to be smashed like a ripe watermelon of complacency on the hard pavement of an entirely new musical genre.

Yes, a storm is brewing. A mighty storm, that will come and wash all the rain off the pavements, though it itself is also rain – but of a different variety perhaps.

But first to the matter in hand. A 'review' of the 'entertainment' on offer.

## The Fangz

The Fangz, darlings of the 2010 mard-core funk fest, have emerged as the smirking champs of C-list uni guitar bands. But was the battle worth winning? This outing suggested otherwise. Consisting as it did of a weary trudge through a three-chord minefield. What profits a band if it wins Chorlton-cum-Hardy but loses its soul?

The Fangz kicked off with guaranteed crowd-pleaser 'Moonfart', and the room, like a lazy cock on a sultry night, began to stiffen in anticipation. But the musical climax of this three-minute meisterwork 'comes' in a joyless orgasm of grey noise, while front man Hugh Jubson (History and French, oh-la-la!) delivers his trademark intonation of a list of victims of the 1919 cholera epidemic in Chicago.

Nice touch, but no cigar.

The rest of the set toyed with a set of tropes so overworked in the Fangz back catalogue that it was a surprise to find the crowd wasn't laughing at the banal repetition of themes such as 'love', 'love gone wrong' and 'cholera in the early nineteenth century'. We get it, guys! Relationships are hard. Water purification is important!

The crowd, of course, did their crowdy thing. Tempting the Fangz into ever greater feats of hubris as they imitated, almost satirically, an audience having a good time. The Fangz didn't get it. They simply wanted to know, 'Are you having a good time?' to which the audience responded, mockingly, 'Yeah,' goading Jubson to further heights of hubris as he then queried, 'Yeah?' and the crowd responded, as surely they must (and did), 'Yeah!'

The crowning piece of ironic fuel at this

horonic inferno was the laughable absence of a rhythm guitar foil in their set-closer 'Kiss Me Kick'. Those of you with long memories will remember that the Fangz autumn (or original) line-up included a certain Kingsley Owen in this role. Educated authorities considered him a success. But now they soldier on, boats against the current, looking like assholes, as someone near me said, and trying manfully, hilariously, stupidly, to ignore the hole his absence has left in their 'sound'.

Jubson, the preening cock, danced about. He's a laughable tyrant, hiring and firing at will, and soon he will be forgotten more than anyone has ever been forgotten, someone near me muttered wisely as they shambled off stage.

★☆☆☆☆

## Kilton's Massive Overload

Kilton are respected. Kilton are revered. Kilton are a bunch of fucking dicks.

There. I've said it. Attendees at their recent 'auditions' for a guitar player to beef up their anaemic post-electro pre-inspiration sound report that at the auditions this West London noise collective's self-appointed leader, third-year beauty Olivia Yar, barely deigned to make conversation with the humble players who strutted and strummed for her pleasure.

They seem to have landed a useful idiot for the role: fat-fingered blunderbuss Paul Wilson. Hark at how his fretwork fumbles. Thrill at his clumsy bridge-mastery!

The set was not short and not in the least sweet. The audience were battered into submission by the subwoofers and began stomping their feet – not to my mind in enjoyment, but more like a band of weary soldiers left far behind enemy lines to trudge

across the whole of Russia before the end of nine-minute dub 'epic' 'Full Fat Cream'.

★★☆☆☆

## Toby Twinings

Ah the delights of a solo songster. Twinings came as a hearty cheese after two heavy helpings of rancid pork rind. But what flavour was the cheese? Because certain observers wondered if it wasn't laced with scorpion or bitter sting of deceit.

The charge? That Twinings' lyrical lament, 'Cold Chinese On A Hot Summer's Night' bears a remarkable, not to say supernatural, similarity to an as yet unperformed work by a certain well-known south Manchester student guitar maestro, once of The Fangz, initials K.O. – you do the math.

The sharp-eyed (but not necessarily wrong) critics who grew in number during the performance asked, could Twinings have spent rather too long around certain dormitory bedrooms as, shall we say, another minstrel was showing their wares? Might he have been fortuitously close to genius in the baked-potato queue as a certain young, talented innocent hummed his melody, unaware of the presence all around of ungrateful magpies? Basically – and I merely report what a large minority of the audience seemed to be mumbling under their breath – could he have stolen the chord structure, elements of melody and a certain vibe from Kingsley Owen's underground phenomenon, 'Implodium Implodes'?

They say imitation is the sincerest form of flattery. Well, all I can say is Twinings is fucking sincere.

★★★☆☆ (ironic)

## Conclusions

A review with a conclusion? Well, yes. For here surely there's a sense of an ending.

The whole evening was in essence a vicious denunciation of everything second- and third-year Manchester student bands think they're seeking to achieve. But could we not, if we peered hard enough into the confusion, see the outlines of what a true music would look like? Perhaps we could?

It would probably be a four-piece with a deeply sexual front man. It would basically be like the Pixies and the Velvets, but so achingly fresh the audience would aflame afresh with delight at the possibilities of art.

They would have no bongos.

# *The Game*: Is It All Fair Game? No, It Isn't, Not Really

## An Investigative Exposé by Kingsley Owen

For a lot of people at university the best way to forget about your insurmountable student debt and the fact that you've most probably got a worthless degree is to worry about sex.

Who's having it? How exactly are they having it? Where do I meet these people and get them to have it with me? So for my first article I thought I'd take a look at one of the resources people use to help answer some of these questions, a book called *The Game*.

For those of you who don't know *The Game*, it's a book about a group of men who call themselves 'pick-up artists' (PUAs) and who try to sleep with women using 'neuro-linguistic programming' (NLP) and 'speed-seduction' (SS) – because apparently there's nothing women love more than acronyms.

Everybody involved claims that the pick-up artist thing is meant to help out desperate guys, but like 'banter' or the Saw films, it's pretty much just an excuse to be a bit misogynistic.

Having said that I've been trying out the various methods outlined in the book for the last couple of weeks – purely for journalistic reasons, of course. If you're going to criticize something you've got to know what you're talking about – I don't want to be like one of those war correspondents who pretends to be in the Fallujah but is actually in a Premier Inn off the M4 with the blinds drawn and *Apocalypse Now* playing in the background.

So here are a few of the so-called 'techniques' and my findings:

### Peacocking

This is when a guy wears an interesting object to stand out from the crowd, like a funny hat or something. To be honest, I think that just makes you look like a bit of a twat – I don't think girls are so fickle that they'll sleep with a guy just because he's wearing a cock-ring as a medallion. I recently tried growing a soul patch and I usually carry around a yo-yo, but those aren't affectations, I'm just genuinely into that sort of stuff.

### Seduction Lair

This is where PUAs meet to discuss their various strategies. To be honest, I think the whole thing is weird enough without adding the phrase 'seduction lair'. Nothing wholesome has ever happened in a 'lair'. Even if you put words that normally have good connotations in front of it, it still ends up sounding pretty evil – I think you'll agree that an 'Ice Cream and Puppies Lair' sounds vaguely ominous.

## Demonstrating Higher Value

Essentially you're meant to do stuff that impresses women and convinces them that you're an attractive guy. The book suggests that you should do something like a magic trick. I think this technique is pretty much nonsense – maybe I'm cynical, but I don't think girls fancy Michael Fassbender because he knows how to pull a penny from behind their ears.

Also, when I was 13 my class had to put on an assembly for the whole school and my contribution was a small magic show. For the rest of the year everybody called me 'Gay Daniels', like Paul Daniels but gay (I went to a pretty average school).

## The Neg

You try and say something that sounds innocuous but is meant to undermine a girl's confidence and lower her self-esteem, like 'I don't care if you've got bags under your eyes, I still think you're pretty.' I decided to try this method out in the student union bar, so I told a girl that she was out of my league, even though she had 'slightly chunky wrists'.

Surprisingly it did sort of work, but not perfectly – I got her number, but now and then for the rest of the night she kept accidentally calling me 'Dad'.

So in conclusion I'd say, read *The Game* and learn all about picking up girls if you really want to, but bear in mind that even if some of the techniques work, you will probably end up feeling a little bit dirty.

It's essentially the dating equivalent of lying to a self-check-out machine about what type of apples you're buying – sure you can get Pink Ladies for the price of Braeburns, but you're probably going to be left with the bitter aftertaste of shame and regret when you finally bite into one.

N.B. I'm not saying that women are defenceless apples that men can just pick up and eat.

# *Blaster* classifieds

## Bassist wanted

Are you a bassist who appreciates the need for a thick, non-fussy bottom-end, but who at the same time can accept his (or her) lowly role as the humble servant to the twin masters of lyrics and melody? Can you subsume your ego and chain yourself to the furnaces of the darkened engine room of the lower octaves? You can? Then I'd like to hear from you. NO time-wasters or five-string bassists. Kingsley on **07888 776524**

## STD CLINIC

The University offers a complete walk-in STD service at the health centre.

Drop in before it drops off.

www.stdclinic/nhsnorthwest.org.uk

## CONFIDENTIAL AND DISCREET

## FOR SALE
### First year psychology books

Only slightly soiled complete collection of first year set texts. Contact *Blaster* classifieds ref: 163/RP02. Or leave a message for Steve on the Psychology Department notice board.

## Rhythm guitarist wanted

Do you want to get rich and tour the world? Or do you want to devote yourself to the gruelling, arduous, backbreaking task of shifting the indie-rock paradigm? If you think you've got the moral and musical fortitude required to help me move mountains with my bare hands, like an indie-rock pharaoh building a pyramid of pure sound, hit me up for an interview. Kingsley on **07888 776524**

House for six people becoming available at the beginning of next term. Near University. Wi-Fi, modern kitchen and Sky TV. Rent on application.

Contact *Blaster* classifieds ref: 163/RP05

## Keyboardist wanted

Wilfully obtuse post-punk quasi-prog audionaut seeks solid, no-bullshit keyboard player for drones and squiggles. Prospective candidates should be prepared for widespread popular lack of interest and belated critical acclaim. (In the interests of full disclosure, I'm not entirely sold on the idea of having a keyboard player in my band. It's up to YOU to make me change my mind.)

Kingsley on **07888 776524**

One-to-one Maths tuition available all evenings, all areas. £10 per hour.
Contact *Blaster* classifieds ref: 163/RP06

French-speaking exchange student is looking for to have conversations with English fluent speaker in public places only, and during daylight hours.
Contact *Blaster* classifieds ref: 163/RP04.

## Drummer wanted

Five things you should know:
1) You'll be actively prohibited from showcasing your repertoire of fills and rolls.
2) You'll be required to keep your shirt on at all times.
3) No one will ever know your name.
4) No one will ever say thank you.
5) In 20 years' time they'll show retrospectives of our seminal works on late-night BBC4 documentaries.

Kingsley on **07888 776524**

# KINGSLEY'S BAND NAMES

## LONG SHORTS

The Apples

### KING KINGSLEY

Give it to Me Straight

12 Month Subscription

## Three Titted Ladies

The GCSEs

## Mouth Wide Shut

## Ska Face

Hepatitis K

THE 1 PER CENT

The Ticket Inspectors

Mazel Tov!

## THE KLASH

Urban Foxes Ate My Baby

*Bit arrogant?*

*Does it sound a bit like a gay cover band?*

*Makes us sound smart*

*Reference to Total Recall, but might sound sexist out of context?*

*Probably won't help us get groupies*

*Might be tricky to look up on Google?*

*Good, but I don't really want to be in a ska band?*

*Sounds elitist?*

*Probably get sued*

# I'M FEELING LUCKY

## FREAKSHOW

## Kony 2012

## The Mercenaries

*— Might be too topical?*

Yes, Doctor?

**Bank Holiday Traffic**

*— Boring?*

## Ready to Die

*Too emo and I'm not ready to die at all* —

*Could be a Christian rock band?*

### The Mini-Disks

# FULL BLOWN RAIDS

... And on the Sixth Day God Created Rock

ROFLCOPTER

*Already a band —*

*Sounds like a kids' band*

## THE SHINS

## 5-4-3-2-Fun!

# KING$LEY

St George is Cross

*— Clever or just confusing? Not sure.*

**Hugh Grant's PA**

*Is this cool?*

# Part Three

# Food & Drink

# Howard's Flowchart 3:
## Schematic for making a cup of tea

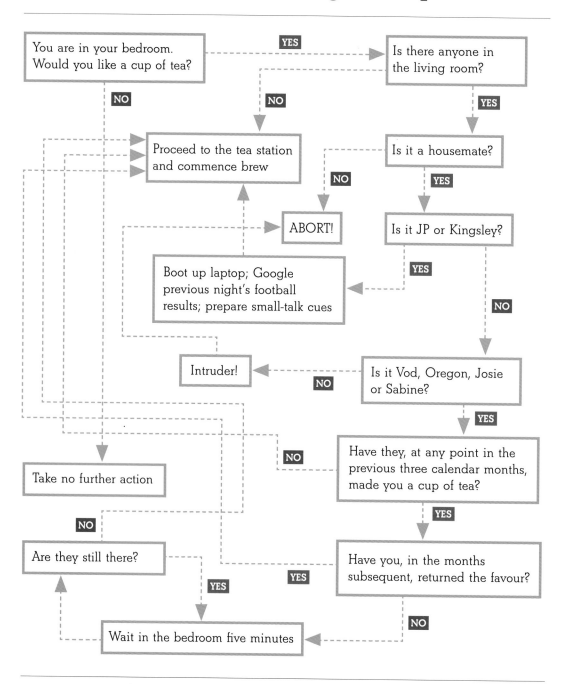

You are in your bedroom. Would you like a cup of tea?

**YES** → Is there anyone in the living room?

**NO** → Proceed to the tea station and commence brew

**NO** → Is it a housemate?

Is there anyone in the living room? **YES** → Is it a housemate?

Is it a housemate? **YES** → Is it JP or Kingsley?

Is it a housemate? **NO** → ABORT!

Is it JP or Kingsley? **YES** → Boot up laptop; Google previous night's football results; prepare small-talk cues

Is it JP or Kingsley? **NO** → Is it Vod, Oregon, Josie or Sabine?

Is it Vod, Oregon, Josie or Sabine? **NO** → Intruder!

Is it Vod, Oregon, Josie or Sabine? **YES** → Have they, at any point in the previous three calendar months, made you a cup of tea?

Have they, at any point in the previous three calendar months, made you a cup of tea? **NO** →

Have they, at any point in the previous three calendar months, made you a cup of tea? **YES** → Have you, in the months subsequent, returned the favour?

Have you, in the months subsequent, returned the favour? **YES** → Wait in the bedroom five minutes

Have you, in the months subsequent, returned the favour? **NO** → Wait in the bedroom five minutes

Are they still there? **NO** → Take no further action

Are they still there? **YES** → Wait in the bedroom five minutes

Take no further action

ABORT!

# Josie's Recipes
## The very best of student cookery

'As the best cook in the house, I have been asked to put together a selection of my favourite recipes. You might like to try these out at home, or simply enjoy reading about how I created them and what inspired each dish.' **Josie Jones**

### Contents
1. Classic Munge
2. Chunge
3. Munge o' Meat
4. Tinned Potato Surprise
5. Fantasia

# Classic Munge

also known as 'Original Munge' or just 'Munge'

Munge was one of those amazing happy accidents that happens when you're improvising in the kitchen! My mum had cooked me some meals to take with me, and by the end of week one, I had a few Tupperware boxes containing leftovers. Each individual pot didn't contain enough to make a meal, so I combined them all, cooked them up, added seasoning, and lo! Munge was born! Since then I've been making it regularly, and it's a favourite with my housemates and visitors. Keep it in the pan, and you can keep reheating and serving fresh portions for up to a week. It's a real student staple.

## Ingredients

Leftovers
Knob of butter
1 tbsp tomato ketchup
Soy sauce
Seasoning

## Equipment

1 x pan

## Instructions

- Heat the knob of butter in the pan, stirring until melted.
- Add your leftovers, the ketchup, the soy sauce and some seasoning. Stir and heat, mashing with the spoon until the firm contours of the foodstuffs begin to break down into a delicious mungelike consistency.
- Always taste your munge, adding more seasoning if necessary. Flavour of munge depends on the nature of the leftovers used.

Serving suggestion

# Chunge

Sometimes, an experiment just 'works'. And this is the case with Chunge, to the extent that it is now – arguably – more popular than the traditional Munge. Cheese lovers who love Munge will find Chunge irresistible.

## Ingredients

Leftovers
Several fistfuls of grated cheese[1]
Knob of butter
1 tbsp tomato ketchup
Soy sauce
Seasoning

## Equipment

1 x pan

## Instructions

- Heat the knob of butter in the pan, stirring until melted.
- Add the leftovers, the ketchup, the soy sauce, some seasoning AND . . . your cheese!
- Follow instructions as for Munge.

---

1. I prefer mild orange economy cheddar, but try this recipe with YOUR favourite cheese – I guarantee it will be cheesylicious (i.e. cheesy AND delicious!)

# Munge o' Meat

A real winter warmer with a meaty twist, this is Munge – but not as you know it.
I first thought of this when frozen chicken pieces were 2 for 1 in Aldi.
The combination of my bargain poultry and the remnants of munge in the
pan were a marriage made in heaven – it tastes divine!

## Ingredients
Diced chicken/beef/lamb
Half an onion
Leftovers
Knob of butter
1 tbsp tomato ketchup
Soy sauce
Seasoning

## Equipment
1 x pan

## Instructions
- Fry the meat and onions in the pan
  using your knob as lubricant. Make sure
  the lumps are brown on all sides.
  NB food poisoning can occur (and indeed
  has occurred) if instructions are not followed
  carefully, so please do cook your meat through!
- Now add your leftovers, ketchup, soy sauce and seasoning. Stir, mulch and mash
  until nice and hot and soft, and until each morsel of meat is fully munge-coated.
- Serve piping hot!

# Tinned Potato Surprise

As a chef, I'm a massive fan of the trusty tin. Did you know that if you were locked in a nuclear bunker for 60 years then most tins would still be OK to eat when you got out? So, in case of an apocalypse, it's always good to have a tin-based recipe to hand. Just because most of humanity has been wiped out, and the future (once the tins run out) looks bleak, doesn't mean you shouldn't enjoy your food.

## Ingredients
- 1 tin potatoes
- 1 tin olives (black)
- 1 tin baked beans

## Equipment
- 1 x pan

## Instructions
- Open the tins of potatoes and olives, and drain away the excess water. Open the tin of beans and add to the saucepan. Heat over a medium heat for several minutes, stirring slowly.
- Add the potatoes and olives, mixing them in with the beans until they are all as hot as each other.
- Pour into a bowl, eat with a fork and enjoy!

# Fantasia

After the best part of three bottles of wine, but no dinner, I went to bed and had a vivid dream in which I was wandering through a strange forest foraging for food. When I woke up, dry-mouthed and be-headached, the recipe for Fantasia was in my brain! Using fresh ingredients such as broccoli and cheese, this dish is probably the most complex of my recipes, so only attempt it if you are pretty confident about your culinary skills. It's worth it, though, as it's packed with dreamy goodness!

## Ingredients

1 jar pasta sauce
5 slices cooked ham
½ a broccoli
½ a block of medium
    cheddar cheese
some rice
water (boiled)

## Equipment

1 x pan

## Instructions

- Cook the rice by boiling it in water.
- While you wait for the rice, chop the ham and broccoli, grate the cheese and open the jar of sauce.
- When the rice is nearly cooked, add the broccoli and boil that too, until soft.
- When both rice and broccoli are ready, drain the remaining water into the sink, using the lid of the pan to stop the contents falling out.
- Return to the heat and add the pasta sauce and ham, stirring until hot. Now grate the cheese and add to the mixture. Don't worry if it melts – it's meant to!
- And that's Fantasia – Mmm, fantastic!

# A Guide to Throwing the Ultimate House Party

(OK, maybe not the 'ultimate' house party, but at least one that's not going to scar anybody for life)

## Q&A with Josie and Vod

Hopefully, a regular highlight of every student's life will be … The House Party. If you've got an older brother or sister, they'll probably have told you a thing or two about university house parties. You might even have heard the odd naughty story – you know, people being sick on the stairs, neighbours banging on the door complaining about the loud music –

Homeless people wandering in and stealing all your laptops, then doing so much ketamine they throw a dog off the roof.

No, Vod, that's never actually happened.

Fucking has, mate. And I've got the lead and collar to prove it.

Well, I've never heard of it happening. No, a house party is a civilized affair –

Yeah, civilized like the zoo. Civilized like the court of Caligula.

A *civilized* affair –

Civilized like the inside of Russell Brand's pants at a strip club.

A civilized affair, made up of a few invited guests –

Plus fifteen hundred randoms your mate Steve met down the dog track then couldn't shake off.

Can I please finish? A civilized affair, made up of a few invited guests, a few of your guests' friends, a few partners and perhaps one or two neighbours you've felt moved to invite out of courtesy.

Or so you can break into their house and steal all their voddy and munchies when you run out.

Vod, can you let me speak, please?

Just saying, mate. I'm not sure you're giving them the full picture, that's all. This ain't some sort of Nancy Mitford cream-tea-on-the-terrace-then-dance-with-the-Duke-before-the-Duchess-of-Devonshire-turns-into-a-pumpkin-at-midnight-champagne-and-strawberries-croquet-fest. This is a house party. You want to know what goes down at a house party, kids? Well, get yourself down the video shop and rent *Animal House*. Then punch yourself in the face for being such an unimaginative twat, return *Animal House* and rent *Armageddon*. OK, done that? Now put Armageddon to one side – it doesn't even begin to cover it, frankly – and bash your head against some exposed brick 50 times whilst wanking off a Doberman, listening to Kraftwerk and stuffing your face with those puddings that got banned in the 80s because they made kids go mental. OK? Done? How are you feeling? Well, that's how you'll feel 45 minutes into your first house party. And you've still got another seven hours to go.

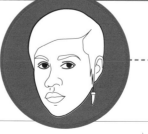

Don't listen to her, everyone. She's just being melodramatic. It's absolutely possible to have a lovely time at a house party without even getting drunk –

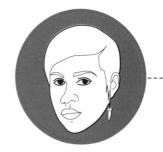

How's that then, Josie? Line dancing? Crochet? Cupcake workshop? Must have missed that memo.

Look, I don't think we're going to agree on any of this.

Nah, mate, I don't think we are.

So why don't we each offer our advice on house parties, then people can choose.

Yeah. Choose to do what I tell them. 'Cos I fucking know what I'm talking about. Whereas you wouldn't know a good party if it broke into your revision class, spiked your Lucozade with meths, then bummed you senseless.

Right. Great. Lovely. OK, guys! Here's . . .

# Josie and Vod's guide to house parties

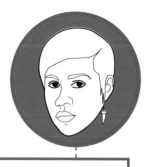

I've broken it down into handy sections so you can flick through and find what you need, when you need it. In fact, you might like to laminate each section and pop it in a folder for reference.

Five people died of boredom while you said that. Just so you know.

Yep. Great. Thanks, Vod. OK – up first ...

## The guest list

Obviously, the guest list is the most important thing of all. Get the mix right and your party could result in lasting friendships, joyful encounters and a good time had by all. And, early on, a house party can be a great way of getting to know new people. If you live in a studenty part of town, perhaps invite some of your neighbours. Otherwise, why not put up a fun poster in a Hall of Residence or faculty building? Be sure to let people know (firmly) what time the party begins and ends, and what they can most usefully bring in the way of food and drink contributions. I know that some people enjoy a 'casual' vibe, but I suggest you get a good RSVP system in place. A few people will RSVP 'yes' but not turn up and a few people will bring surprise plus ones, so it should all even out in the end. But forewarned is forearmed! I'd also strongly advise you and your co-hosts to get a 'door rota' going, so there's always somebody manning the entrance. If you plan carefully, it's unlikely you'll be bothered by too many undesirables, but it's good to have somebody assertive there, just in case.

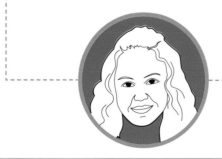

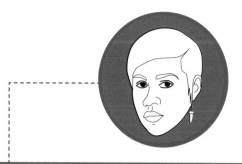

Don't bother. Do not fucking bother. By 10 p.m. your 'guest list' will be about as relevant as the wedding vows of a rock-bottoming sex addict and his smackhead fiancée. You've gotta get zen about this, right? It's an open house. Whoever will be, will be. Keith Chegwin, David Cameron or a gang of randoms who've got lost on their way to a stag night in Billa-fucking-ricay. Leave it up to the gods of lash. And, frankly, the weirder the better. The best uni party I've ever been to ended with the Professor of Chinese Philosophy playing beer-pong with Skanky Pete from down the Chicken Hut (and – all credit to him – winning).

So, yeah, I could give you a load of guff about getting the balance of girls and boys right, making sure there's a dealer for every junkie, etc., etc., but I'm not going to patronize you. It'll sort itself out. And, hopefully, by the end of the evening everyone'll be humping everything in sight and people'll be literally inventing their own drugs.

There are only two types of people you need to watch out for:

**A. Undercover cops.** For obvious reasons. You can usually tell an undercover cop by their woefully inadequate attempts to do 'party behaviour', i.e. standing in the corner with a Corona bopping daddishly to the Wu-Tang Clan, and randomly sticking both hands in the air and shouting, 'Woo, yeah, great pardeee!' at weirdly regular intervals. If you see someone behaving like this, then eject him or her immediately and forcefully. It might mean you accidentally eject a member of the Geology faculty or someone's boyfriend from home, but so be it. Better safe than sorry.

**B. Evangelical Christians.** Very sneaky. They'll slip in undetected – usually bringing some medium-posh crisps, i.e. baked parsnip Kettle Chips, with them and be quiet as mice till about 1 a.m., when they'll start going up to anyone who looks completely off their knob on mushrooms or acid and telling them about the big bloke in the sky with a beard who wants them for a sunbeam. Sounds harmless; actually very, very dangerous. It happened to my mate Moz at a barn rave in Newton Abbot in 2002 and now he's living in a colony married to a nineteen-stone Anabaptist called Raeleen. So, yeah. Beware the God Squad.

## Alcohol

It's pretty widely accepted that people will bring a bottle or two to a house party, so you needn't worry too much about having enough alcohol for everyone. However, it might be wise to keep an 'emergency stash' – perhaps a wine box and a fruity mixer for making sangria – in a locked cupboard somewhere, just in case. Sangria's a great drink, in general – it gets the party started without anyone ending up too merry too soon. I'd also suggest beer and any fizzy wine that you can mix with fruit juice. Some people might scoff at this, but they'll be thanking you the next morning!

Alcohol is very potent stuff – please drink responsibly.

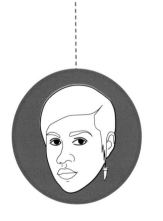

Stay away from white spirit (or anything in the paint-stripper family). It might feel like a bright idea at the time, but I promise, it eats right through your innards, even if you mix it with turpentine. Likewise, meths. Not worth the trouble. If you really are stuck for a drink at five in the morning then you're better off wandering down the park and raiding the passed-out tramps' tins (watch out for fag butts and piss).*

After a certain point in the evening, it's basically all about good chunder management. At any decent house party, at least 70% of your guests will be chundering by midnight, and 10% of those will have gone projectile. You're not going to get it all in the garden/bogs so focus on damage limitation – i.e. better the sink than the sofa. Top tip: if someone looks like they're going to hurl, don't let them anywhere near a trampoline. Nothing worse than popping on for a bounce two days later and finding yourself ankle-deep in gut-slurry.

Oh, and if children are present, make sure you've got enough Bacardi Breezers in. Blue for boys, pink for girls. Bit cute, I know, but it warms my heart every time I see it.

* Obviously, I'm not actually recommending this. But, as I say, anything to keep you off the meths.

## Food

Vitally important to keep your party well fed. I'd recommend something hearty to soak up the booze, perhaps a nice bean stew (like my special Munge!). And maybe you could leave bowls of crisps around the house, or even cocktail sausages or meatballs on toothpicks, if you're feeling flush.

And it might be fun to round off the evening with a dessert item. This also sends a very clear signal to your guests that it's nearly home time. I once went to a golden wedding anniversary in Wales where the happy couple actually hired an ice-cream van to arrive at the end of the evening – it was literally one of the most exciting and unforgettable moments of my life.

Hmm … Nurishment's quite good, I think, or Complan, or any of the meal-replacement stuff. I mean, not for fun eating, just if someone's gone a bit too far into the K-hole and needs something milky to tempt them back out again. Also Monster Munch (though obvs keep all monster graphics/references away from anyone who's on acid). Otherwise, if people want food then they should have gone to a fucking restaurant, shouldn't they? This is a party, mate. There ain't no buffets in hell.

## Entertainment and decorations

Very straightforward. Just plug in an iPod and put it on shuffle – no need for clowns and balloons here. (Though if you want to blow up balloons, then I'm not going to stop you – it's important you be creative, if you feel the need.) Perhaps you could buy a couple of lava lamps from a charity shop, or at least some cheerful cushion covers. My advice is keep it low key, and have fun!

If you've got anything worth over £100 or of any sentimental value at all, either sling a tarpaulin over it or put it in the shed. It's gonna get beasted. Everything's gonna get beasted. Your house is over, mate.

As far as 'entertainment' is concerned, no Berlin electronica before midnight and anyone who puts on S Club 'as a joke' gets tied naked to a fucking bollard 15 miles away in the rain. That's all I'm saying. Figure the rest out for yourselves.

Just the one decorative tip: curtains burn surprisingly quickly. I'm serious. It's weird – you've just gotta show them a flame and whoomph, up they go. So probs best to take them away if it looks like things are getting a bit 'flamey'. Cover the windows with cardboard boxes instead – it creates a nice vibe.

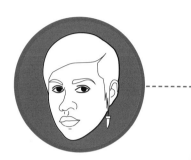

## Disasters

No matter how carefully you plan, there's always the possibility that things will go wrong. Not enough guests turn up, the drinks run out just as the shops have closed or the party simply never takes off. My advice: just laugh about it. You've learned a good lesson, and you'll know not to make the same mistakes next time. OK? It really is no biggie.

I've seen a few ripe old party disasters in my time. Obviously, I can't give away too much (for legal reasons), but let's just say that Quentin Tarantino may well be basing his next film on something I did outside the Greater Manchester Police Sports and Social Club halfway through Freshers' Week. And the only thing I can honestly tell you is that if something goes wrong at a party you've thrown, you will be damaged for ever. Drugs bust, punch-up, mysterious death; your life's ruined. Everything's ruined. You have failed the Party Test, and you will literally never be the same again. Despair.

## Rules and regulations

Absolutely vital. Have a meeting with your co-hosts six weeks before the party and establish your ground rules. I would suggest, as a starting point, a five-drink maximum (there's potential for a drinks token system here), a couple of designated 'chill-out rooms' and a strict ban on all drug taking. Other rules about food rotas, cleaning up, etc. you can figure out amongst yourselves. Have fun!

ARE YOU FUCKING KIDDING ME? Right, that's it. I'm off. If whoever made up these topics ever throws a party, then leave the fucking country. OK?

# Vod's Hangover Recovery Sheet

All right, guys, Oregon asked me to put some shit together for this thing, so I thought I'd stick in my fool-proof hangover cure – that way you can all look at this when you're coming down from your next big night out.

This is pretty much every trick I've picked up over the last few years. It basically turns getting through a hangover into a fucking spa weekend, listening to Enya and getting seaweed wrapped on yer tits.

## Stick on some chilled-out music

Don't worry about it being any good, just pick something that's easy to listen to, like Paolo Nutini – to be honest, the shitter the music the better it seems to work. But remember, if you listen to the same stuff too much your body will start associating it with feeling hungover. Nowadays, every time I hear a Michael Bublé song I want to fucking throw up, and I used to kind of like him.

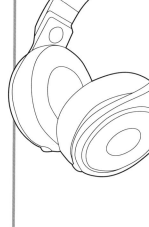

## Wear soft, loose clothes

A hoodie and pyjama bottoms are fucking perfect if you're trying to climb out of an MDMA cave, but make sure you put a time limit on it. There's no excuse for wearing fucking slippers outside the house a day and a half later – it's only a hangover, not a fucking lobotomy.

## Zone out in front of the TV

You want to ride out the darkest shit and give your head time to get back to normal, so just plant yourself in front of something safe, like a *Friends* marathon or VH1. But if you're coming down from mushrooms or something, it's probably best to give the television a miss altogether – you don't want to start channel-surfing and then hit on something that'll fuck with your head, like *The Village*. When I was 16 I went to a weed café in Amsterdam and they were showing, like, the Dutch version of *The Bill* – after three fucking strong pot-lollies I walked into a police station and just started crying.

## Don't be a pussy

Listening to someone bitch and moan about how hungover they're feeling is about as much fun as a fire in a maternity ward. Nobody – not even your best friends – want to listen to you jizz on about having a shitty headache or the fact that it hurts to move your tongue or whatever. Remember, it's your fault that your head feels like a crushed bollock, so just deal with it (unless your drink was spiked or something, in which case, yeah, you can probably kick up a bit of a fuss).

Anyway, just keep a copy of this in your back pocket and go get royally fucked up!

So that's about it, everything you need to know to get over a heavy night of booze, drugs, rock 'n' roll, sex and whatever other sick shit you can get your hands on.

To be honest, I don't know why this isn't on the fucking A-level syllabus – it'd be a lot more useful to kids than reading bloody *Animal Farm*. Why do I have to read 180 pages about fucking pigs when you can just say communism might not work? Seriously, Orwell can shove his parables up his dystopian arsehole.

Part Four

# Making Your Money Last

# The Anatomy of the Cow
## An insider's guide

By Howard MacCallum

On my first day of part-time work at the abattoir, my line manager, a thick-set, balding man with a ruby-red nose known simply as 'Alan', sat me down and told me straight: 'You'll learn more in six months working in this meat-processing plant than you will in ten bloody years at that university.' This has subsequently proven to be false. Nonetheless, I have learned a limited number of things about the anatomy of a cow . . .

**Eyes:** avoid looking into these at any stage during the cow-dispatching process. If working in and around the face and this proves difficult, think about pulling the eyelids closed.

**Cheek:** ideal bulking agent for 'loose sausage'.

**Tongue:** was once slapped in face with severed cow's tongue by a rogue colleague. Unable to eat it since.

**Lips:** am strangely prone to a recurring cow-dream involving TV commercial for bovine range of lipsticks and cosmetics. Have therefore asked Alan to be excused from all future lip work.

**Front leg:** I once returned home and opened my backpack to discover a dismembered left foreleg by way of 'workplace banter'. We certainly do know how to have a good laugh.

In summary, I would say that abattoir work makes for an interesting, if not always enjoyable, choice for the humble student looking for part-time work. If you're of a delicate psychological disposition, and you don't relish the thought of sawing through bone, my advice would be to try your local video shop.

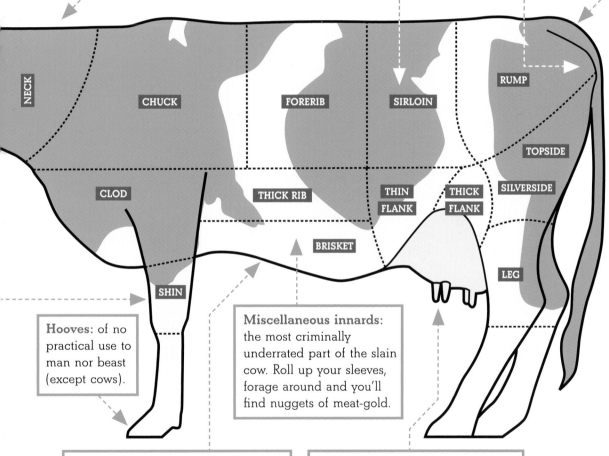

**Neck:** during a slow day on the killing floor, I was once invited to use a bolt-gun to stun a cow. I've been partially successful in repressing all memories (how heavy the gun felt; the thin cracking sound, etc).

**Tail:** another popular instrument of misadventure. Have seen a human male skipping with two cow tails taped together.

**Sirloin:** one of the 'snooty meats', along with brisket, rump and silverside. Though perhaps smoother on the palette than the 'value meats' (lips, cheek, anus), not necessarily more filling.

**Anus:** unpleasant in its natural context; makes perfectly adequate beef paste.

NECK

CHUCK

FORERIB

SIRLOIN

RUMP

TOPSIDE

CLOD

THICK RIB

THIN FLANK

THICK FLANK

SILVERSIDE

BRISKET

LEG

SHIN

**Hooves:** of no practical use to man nor beast (except cows).

**Miscellaneous innards:** the most criminally underrated part of the slain cow. Roll up your sleeves, forage around and you'll find nuggets of meat-gold.

**Intestine:** mostly liquidized during the 'evisceration process'. The resulting 'beef smoothie' is noticeably less pleasant than it sounds.

**Udder:** along with the tongue, this is the cow part most frequently used for abattoir-based tomfoolery.

# Howard's Ten Money-Saving Tips

In these economically troubled times it's more important than ever that we students keep an eye on the bottom line. If you follow these ten simple tips, you'll find that you can have a great lifestyle and a healthy bank balance! Howard.

## 1. Bake a 1.5-metre flapjack

The first rule of money saving. You will need:

- 4kg oats
- 2.75kg margarine
- 4kg Demerara sugar (or approx. 250 coffee-house sugar sachets)
- 1.5kg low-grade golden syrup
- A rectangular container 1.5m in length
- An airing cupboard with sufficient space to store a 1.5m flapjack. (Mine is currently stored upright, propped between the ironing board and the clothes horse.)

**FIGURE.01** Each square represents one 'meal'.

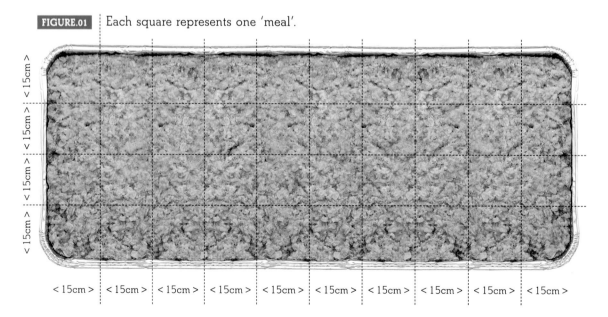

< 15cm > < 15cm > < 15cm > < 15cm > < 15cm > < 15cm > < 15cm > < 15cm > < 15cm > < 15cm >

Once the flapjack is baked to your satisfaction, cut it into 15cm squares. Each square represents a 'meal'. If you take three meals a day, and assuming your container is at least 60cm in width (giving you a total edible surface area of $0.9m^2$), you'll easily have enough to last you a full fortnight. That's two weeks' 'eating' for the price of a Marks & Spencer ready meal.

## 2. Isolate yourself from your social peers

Think about it – the fewer friends you have, the less likely you are to be invited to do things. Try to cultivate a reputation in the first term for being difficult or prickly, with sudden shifts in mood and temper. You'll thank me for it come term three when your student loan has long since been frittered away and you're being pressured to attend a never-ending programme of financially crippling social occasions and birthday parties (with attendant gift/card costs). Also, by leaving the house less you'll significantly lower the number of times you get mugged per annum, saving you cool, hard coin.

## 3. Switch to role-playing games

Spurn big-budget action-adventure video games with meagre eight-hour playing times in favour of sprawling, open-ended, role-playing games. The maths is simple:

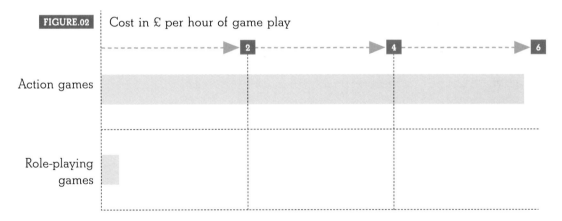

FIGURE.02 Cost in £ per hour of game play

That's a value-tastic twenty pence per hour. Prioritize those role-playing games with a high element of 'grinding'; the 'grind' being the repetitive slaying of virtual beasties in return for tiny, incremental increases of experience points or gold coins. Though mind-numbingly tedious, like low-paid menial factory work, 'grinding' is nonetheless technically still interactive entertainment, and as such legally constitutes a perfectly valid way to spend evenings and weekends.

## 4. Try your hand at 'free-stooling'

For the uninitiated, 'free-stooling' is the practice of defecating exclusively in municipal lavatories, thereby liberating yourself from the mounting costs of toilet paper, sewerage charges ('flush-fees') and one-off bog-brush expenditure. Here's how it works: over the past twelve months, by carefully moderating my diet, I have been able to sync my movements to coincide with my academic timetable. I'm thus able to 'free-stool' in the university toilets between seminars.

Wednesdays in particular are a challenge as I don't have any classes, but by eating a highly binding three-egg omelette on Tuesday evening, I can coast through the mid-week break before 'free-stooling' again at 8.45 a.m. on Thursday, immediately before Glacial Environments. Sure, it's not for everyone. It requires planning, forethought and at times an almost iron will (it also helps if you live near a Debenhams with late-night shopping), but the rewards are obvious. As for me, I recently completed the entire spring term without having to resort to 'home-stooling' once.

## 5. Take full advantage of Starbucks' complimentary milk stations

Out shopping and feeling a bit parched? Locate your nearest Starbucks and head over to their complimentary milk station for a glass of semi-skimmed on the house. While you're there, help yourself to a couple of sachets of Demerara (perfect for 1.5m flapjack) and a handful of wooden stirrers (ideal as bookmarks). Once you've slaked your thirst with a gratis glass of the white stuff, why not grab a paper from the rack and take a 'free-stool' in their plush, three-trap facilities?

## 6. Sock it to them

Slash your annual sock bill in half by learning the power of one simple phrase: 'May I borrow a pair of socks?' The number of people who will loan you a pair of socks and then effectively write them off, never daring or wishing to ask for them back, constantly surprises me. See right for my 2011/12 figures:

My sock drawer is like a meeting of the United Nations, with representatives from as far afield as Nottingham, Belfast, Northampton and even Holland. You'll never go barefoot again.

**FIGURE.03**

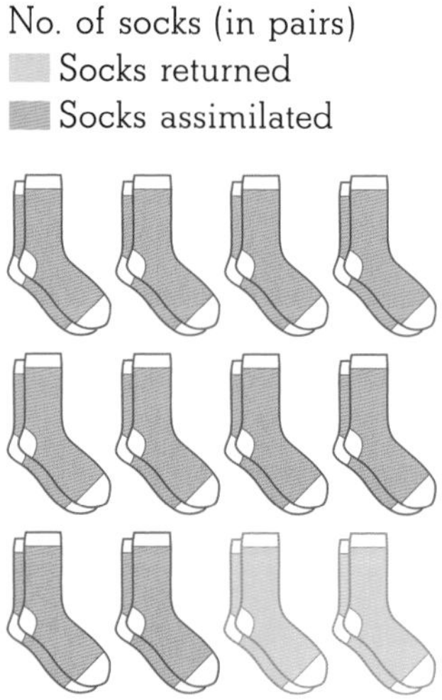

No. of socks (in pairs)
Socks returned
Socks assimilated

## 7. Disconnect yourself from popular culture

I currently have some 'blocking software' installed on my computer, the kind a sex addict might use to restrict the number of hours he can spend trawling the internet for grot. 'Howard, are you trying to tell us something?' I hear you cry. 'No,' I reply quite seriously, 'I have no interest in seeing both men and women being degraded because it degrades me too.'

My blocking software is in fact configured to prohibit me from accessing movie news websites. With no idea of what films are currently in development I deny myself the chance to become emotionally attached to certain projects, and therefore no longer feel obliged to shell out £8.50 on the day of release. Instead, I'll sit down at my laptop, read a full and forensic plot synopsis while munching on popcorn and looking at the occasional production still. Bliss.

## 8. Avoid any rapid forms of physical exertion

I've found that by decreasing my default walking pace by 10% and avoiding any unnecessary rapid, sudden movements, I'm able to regulate my perspiration and thereby limit the number of costly laundry cycles per week. Granted, you might miss the odd bus and be late for the occasional seminar, but your bank manager will thank you.

## 9. Treat your friendly newsagent as though it were a library

Exploit the meek disposition of your friendly local newsagent (who's still recovering from the armed robbery visited upon him six weeks ago, and who seems to view everyone under the age of 25 as a hoodlum) by reading the latest video-game magazines entirely without charge, straight from the newsstand.

## 10. Open your mind, meat-wise

There are certain misnomers and urban myths about which parts of a cow you can and cannot eat (see The Anatomy of the Cow: An Insider's Guide, p.176). Check your inhibitions in at the door, forget everything you thought you knew about food hygiene and roll with it. My rule when eating the 'grey meats' is simple: don't ask if you don't want to know. And anyway, I've found that the human body is the best regulator of what is and isn't an acceptable piece of cow to digest. So rustle yourself a bowl of Meatabix, and suck it and see!

# Weekly house shopping list — essentials

- Molton Brown black pepper shower gel
- Alford and Hoff SPF 15 Hydrating Cream
- red snapper
- brioche
- fennel/s
- red onion and sage focaccia
- Reflets de France black tapenade
- artichoke hearts
- Maximuscle Promax high protein meal bars x12
- Maximuscle Progain high protein shake (7kg)
- any decent duck and port terrine
- serdelki (emulsified smoked Polish sausage)
- 40 Marly Lights
- a grouse

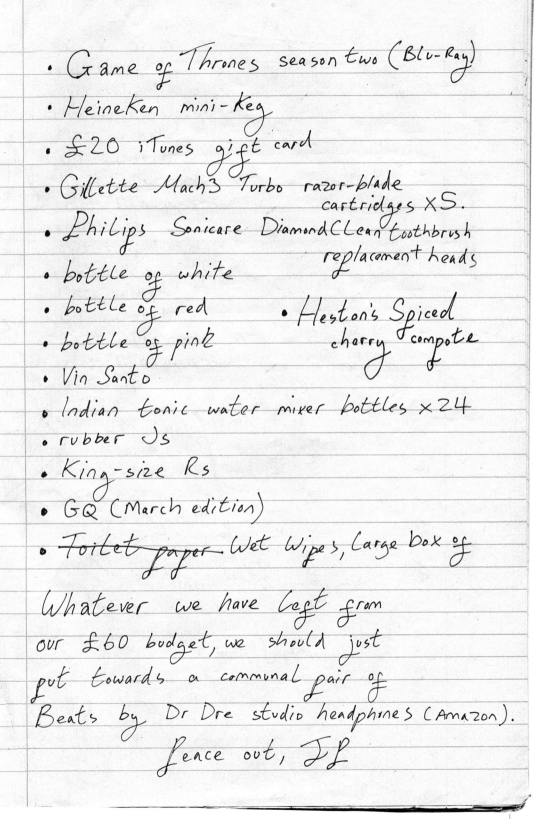

- Game of Thrones season two (Blu-Ray)
- Heineken mini-keg
- £20 iTunes gift card
- Gillette Mach3 Turbo razor-blade cartridges x5.
- Philips Sonicare DiamondClean toothbrush replacement heads
- bottle of white
- bottle of red
- bottle of pink
- Heston's Spiced cherry compote
- Vin Santo
- Indian tonic water mixer bottles x24
- rubber Js
- King-size Rs
- GQ (March edition)
- ~~Toilet paper~~ Wet wipes, large box of

Whatever we have left from our £60 budget, we should just put towards a communal pair of Beats by Dr Dre studio headphones (Amazon).

Peace out, JL

# JP's Million-Dollar-Idea Ideas

These are ideas I've had which are – quite literally (and also figuratively) – million-dollar ideas. As in, they're going to earn me a m****rfu**ing million dollars (or pounds) in my lifetime if I put them into action, which I totally will. Which is why you won't see me giving any kind of a toss about that 'careers' bullshit. I'm sorted, mate. Get over it.

**NB: ALL OF THE IDEAS BELOW ARE COPYRIGHTED OR ARE ABOUT TO BE COPYRIGHTED, SO IF YOU PINCH THEM I WILL SUE YOUR ARSE. MY UNCLE IS A TOP BARRISTER SO WATCH OUT. CHEERS.**

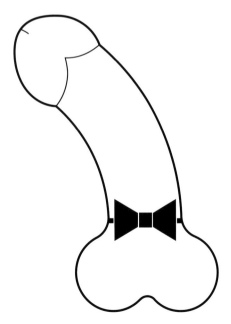

## The Dressticle

I'm not yet 100% certain what this is, but the title alone makes it worth pursuing. It's probably a little costume for your bollock – or bollocks. Could create some kind of standard 'mould' thing, (variety of sizes/shapes), then the Dressticle could be tailored for either practical use, e.g. warmth, or recreational use, e.g. stag nights/erotica. Available in a variety of fabrics such as PVC/leather for fetishists; cotton/polyester for the mid-market; tweed/Barbour jacket material for the Home Counties. But always lined with something nice and soft.

**INVESTMENT REQUIRED:** £200K.
**WILL MAKE IN FIRST YEAR:** a couple of mil, at least.

## Website that's also a mirror

But a true mirror. This is not like Instagram or Apple Photo Booth or one of those applications that lets you see what you'd look like in the 1850s or if you were obese. No way. Just a straightforward mirror. It's so retro it's basically progressive. www.mirror.com or something. Shazam!

**INVESTMENT REQUIRED:** £500 max. Just the domain name and some random techie to make shit happen.

**WILL MAKE IN FIRST YEAR:** A mil.

## Warm deodorant

'Tired of that terrible cold blast on your pits morning after morning after morning? Yeah, me too. Very much so. Why is deodorant always so damned cold?! Well, shiver no more, my friend, with the all-new warm deodorant!' Don't quite know how it'll work yet – I'll let the egg-heads figure that one out thanks – but defo either stuff that comes out of the can already warm (possibly warmed by the energy of the atoms rubbing together or something?), or some kind of little sleeve you can put round the can to warm it. Maybe using the same mechanism as those cans of self-warming soup/coffee?

**INVESTMENT REQUIRED:** £150K.

**WILL MAKE IN FIRST YEAR:** 15 mil.

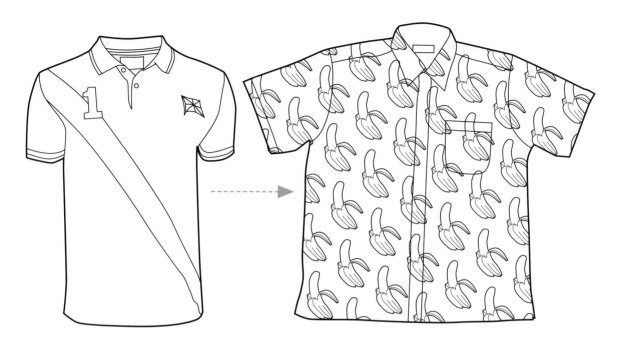

## 'Ironcierge'

**(or poss 'Ironicierge' or 'Ironic-cierge', defo needs to stress that it's an awesome mash-up of 'ironic' and 'concierge')**

A high-end concierge service that delivers, on demand, an 'ironic' version of your life. Ironcierge staff will come round and complete a basic psychological profile of you and your friends, with particular emphasis on that which you look down on/despise/ think is totally hilarious and lame. Then they'll come and replace key items in your life, e.g. trainers, cookware, laptop etc. with versions that you would claim are ironic. For example, if you're a massive leftie vegetarian who gives money to PETA, then Ironcierge will come and replace your watercolour art with a fuck-off massive 'ironic' moose head, and your *Guardian* with an 'ironic' *Daily Mail* and your cheese with 'ironic' steak, leading to mirth amongst you and your mates that could, theoretically, continue for at least three to six months. This is a high-end service that will be best received by the financial and media elite.

**INVESTMENT REQUIRED:** £500K.

**WILL MAKE IN FIRST YEAR:** 10 mil (rich people pay shit-loads for shit like this – I've seen it happen).

## Some way of harnessing the power of magpies to help people find lost phones/keys etc.

Haven't really thought about this yet, but there must be a way.

**INVESTMENT REQUIRED:** Whatever it costs to catch a few magpies and have scientists do shit to them.

**WILL MAKE IN FIRST YEAR:** A mil, no probs.

## Weddings in the tundra

Service providing weddings in largely unpopulated, hostile areas of the earth. People are always looking for original ways to get married.

**INVESTMENT REQUIRED:** £100K.

**WILL MAKE IN FIRST YEAR:** 5 mil.

## Wedding in a war zone

See above. Too much?

**INVESTMENT REQUIRED:** Depends on the war zone.

**WILL MAKE IN FIRST YEAR:** A mil.

## A cup that has magic mushrooms/the hallucinogenic essence of magic mushrooms embedded in the china

Though maybe they should be tin cups, so they're suitable for picnics.

**INVESTMENT REQUIRED:** £500K.

**WILL MAKE IN FIRST YEAR:** A mil.

## Rattlesnake orchestra

**INVESTMENT REQUIRED:** Not sure. Need to phone zoo.

**WILL MAKE IN FIRST YEAR:** Again, not sure, but definitely as much as that ukulele orchestra, probably more!

# The Bosch Papers

The May/June exam corridor can put the student mind under an almost intolerable pressure. Some take it in their stride, studying hard while finding time to socialize on their way to a solid First in Comparative Literature. Others aren't so lucky. Sometimes the strain can prove almost too much to bear, as this document, retrieved from Howard's laptop and simply entitled 'The Bosch Papers', would seem to prove . . .

Oregon x

Oregon

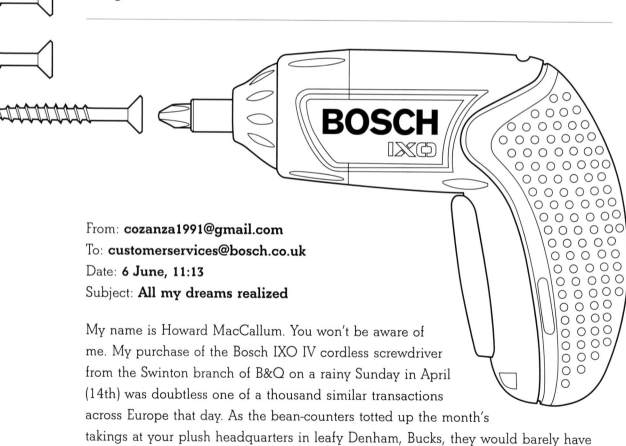

From: **cozanza1991@gmail.com**
To: **customerservices@bosch.co.uk**
Date: **6 June, 11:13**
Subject: **All my dreams realized**

My name is Howard MacCallum. You won't be aware of me. My purchase of the Bosch IXO IV cordless screwdriver from the Swinton branch of B&Q on a rainy Sunday in April (14th) was doubtless one of a thousand similar transactions across Europe that day. As the bean-counters totted up the month's takings at your plush headquarters in leafy Denham, Bucks, they would barely have given a second glance to a tatty receipt for £39.99, paid in full with cash.

And yet . . .

And yet . . .

The product I cradle in my hand (I'm typing with one hand) has transformed me. The power of a Porsche, the sleek lines of a Sunseeker, truly, this is a cordless electric screwdriver for the ages.

I'd read the reviews. Sure I had. I'd stalked my prey for months, even going so far as to download the operating manual in PDF format in order to familiarize myself with its functionality to avoid any surprises on the day of purchase. (I don't like surprises.)

To my eternal shame, I'd discounted much of the online hyperbole re: the IXO IV as yet more pro-Bosch fanboyism. How wrong I was.

How very wrong indeed . . .

The build quality, the trigger action, the soft whirr of the deceptively ferocious 3.6v motor . . . It soon became clear to me, mere moments after gently prising my IXO from the snug crib of its sturdy Bosch-green carry-case, that I was in the presence of a Lithium-Ion power tool beyond even my most fevered imaginings.

So thank you, Bosch. Were I a man of more generous means I would enclose a cheque for an additional £20, for I am of the opinion that your £39.99RRP is almost offensively generous. Alas, I am but a poor student. I hope my undying admiration and gratitude will suffice as meagre recompense.

Howard MacCallum

P.S. I appreciate how busy you all must be with the spring trade-show season, so I don't expect a reply.

From: **customerservices@bosch.co.uk**

To: **cozanza1991@gmail.com**

Date: **7 June, 10:13**

Subject: re: **All my dreams realized**

Dear Howard,

We're delighted to hear you're so happy with your IXO IV electric screwdriver.

We'd like to send you out a complimentary gift bundle in recognition of your valued custom. Please send me your address and we'll get it sent out straight away.

Dale Burrows

Customer Care Assistant

From: **cozanza1991@gmail.com**
To: **customerservices@bosch.co.uk**
Date: **7 June, 10:20**
Subject: **Mind = blown**

Dale,

When I entered into this dialogue, I did so with no other intention than to relay my humble thanks to a German engineering giant that had, in one fell swoop, restored my faith in the future of mass-market handheld power tools.

And so it is with no little surprise that I find myself at my laptop, engaging directly with Bosch itself, soon to be on the receiving end of one 'complimentary gift bundle'. I can find no other way to describe my current state than to say, with no hint of whimsy or irony, that I am positively giddy with excitement.

28 Hartnell Road,
Manchester,
M60 5EP.

FYI – I am still very much enjoying getting to know my IXO IV. Last night, purely for the fun of it, I used the 6mm flat-head attachment to take apart my PlayStation3. That I am still struggling to put it back together again is in no way a reflection of your treasured creation.

From: **cozanza1991@gmail.com**
To: **customerservices@bosch.co.uk**
Date: **8 June, 14:23**
Subject: **Tracking number**

Hi Dale,

Just wondering if you had a Post Office tracking number for the 'complimentary gift bundle' – 28 hours later and no sign of it this end . . .

I've just had a horrible vision of a rogue Post Office employee clocking the Bosch livery on the package and cracking it open for himself, spilling the bounty contained within onto the damp concrete floor of the sorting office . . .

From: **cozanza1991@gmail.com**
To: **customerservices@bosch.co.uk**
Date: **9 June, 16:23**
Subject: **Concern**

With packages, as with missing children, the first 72 hours are critical. It's now a Saturday. Tomorrow is a Sunday. This means we are losing vital time . . .

Re-reading your email dated 6 June, you clearly specified the bundle was to be sent out 'straight away'. Allowing for the internal Bosch mail-run to occur at no later than 4.30 p.m., and noting that our exchange took place at 10.20 a.m., I can only assume that you had ample time to mail it out that day. All of which leads me to assume that a heinous act of parcel-based criminality has been visited upon my person. Please, at your earliest convenience, call me on my mobile.

From: **cozanza1991@gmail.com**
To: **customerservices@bosch.co.uk**
Date: **10 June, 17:29**
Subject: **Confusion**

I feel jittery and I'm finding it hard to concentrate for long periods. I've also noticed a shortness of breath. I can only assume these are the side-effects of some kind of mail-fraud-related stress disorder. Tired. So, so, so tired . . .

From: **cozanza1991@gmail.com**
To: **customerservices@bosch.co.uk**
Date: **11 June, 04:03**
Subject: **Reflections**

Have you ever noticed the way cats seem to dance through the rain, never getting a drop on them?

I'm at my window, waiting for a postman I know will never come. Maybe it's the whiskey, maybe it's the fullness of the moon, maybe it's the fact that my PS3 still isn't working . . . somehow everything just seems clear to me.

There is no 'complimentary gift bundle'. There never was . . .

So hearty congrats. You got me. You got me good. (contd.)

Bosch: 1, Howard Mackenzie MacCallum: 0.

What is it they say? Never meet your idols? Well, I've looked into the face of Bosch corporation, I've stared hard into those cold, dead eyes, and I've seen nothing but hatred, fear, contempt and tardiness.

You're out there somewhere, Dale. Tucked up in your double bed with your gorgeous wife, lost to peaceful slumbers. I wonder what it is you dream about, Dale Burrows. Do you dream in colour, or are you like a dog, trapped in dim monochrome?

For the record, having lived with it for nigh on a week, what's becoming increasingly apparent to me is that the IXO IV is actually a pretty ordinary portable screwdriver. The forward/reverse switch is too close to the trigger and the battery-life is frankly disappointing.

So good night, Dale; good night, Bosch; good night to all and to all a good night . . .

From: **cozanza1991@gmail.com**
To: **customerservices@bosch.co.uk**
Date: **12 June, 09:03**
Subject: **Closure**

Morning Dale,

I know you probably don't feel like hearing from me right now, but just to give you some closure, I thought I'd let you know my complimentary gift bundle arrived this morning.

Thank you. The Bosch-branded rubber and ruler set will come in handy with my studies.

All the best for the future,
Howard.